MYSTERY MAZE

James Barry
Christine McClymont
Glen Huser

© Nelson Canada,
A Division of Thomson Canada Limited, 1993

Published in 1993 by
Nelson Canada,
A Division of Thomson Canada Limited
1120 Birchmount Road
Scarborough, Ontario M1K 5G4

ISBN 0-17-603944-9

Project Manager: Lana Kong
Project Editor: Tara Shields
Senior Production Editor: Deborah Lonergan
Art Direction: Bruce Bond
Cover Design: Liz Nyman
Cover Illustration: Jamie Bennett
Series Design: Janet Riopelle

Printed and bound in Canada.

234567890 /WC/ 21098765

Canadian Cataloguing in Publication Data
Main entry under title:
Mystery maze
(Nelson mini-anthologies)

ISBN 0-17-603944-9

1. Readers (Secondary). 2. Detective and mystery stories.
I. Barry, James, 1939- . II. Huser, Glen, 1943-
III. McClymont, Christine. IV. Series.

PN6071.D45M9 1993   428.6   C93-093401-6

Series Review Panel

Table of Contents

1

WHAT'S THE CRIME?

The Chocolate Mousse
Murder . . . . CARTOON 7
Marty Norman

Bog Body . . . . ARTICLE 8
Katherine Grier

Live Music . . . . STORY 11
Adèle Geras

The Boy From Nowhere . . . . ARTICLE 22
William Warren

The Summer of the Beautiful
White Horse . . . . STORY 32
William Saroyan

Midnight . . . . POEM 44
Baljit Kang

2

JUSTICE WITH A TWIST

My Aunt . . . . POEM 45
Ted Hughes

Two Stories to Solve:
Outwitting the King, The Bet . . . PUZZLES 47
George Shannon

Lamb to the Slaughter . . . . STORY 51
Roald Dahl

Twins . . . . STORY 67
Eric Wright

3

DETECTIVES TO THE RESCUE

**Origin of the Detective
Business** . . . . SATIRE 75
Newton Newkirk

The Big Holdup . . . . CARTOON PUZZLE 78
Martin Gardner

The Punchboards . . . . STORY 81
Henry T. Parry

Fingerprints Tell Tales . . . . ARTICLE 97
Martha G. Webb

**The Case of the Dentist's
Patient** . . . . PUZZLE . . . 100
Donald J. Sobol

Puzzle for Poppy . . . . STORY . . . 102
Patrick Quentin

Strange Jest . . . . STORY . . . 124
Agatha Christie

1

What's the Crime?

▲▼▶▼▷▲▼▷▼▲▼▷▼▲▼▷▼▲▼▷▼▶

THE CHOCOLATE MOUSSE MURDER

by Marty Norman

▲▼►▼►▲▼►▼▲▼►▼►▲▼►▼►

BOG BODY

by Katherine Grier

When Danish farmers found a body in a bog, they thought they had discovered the victim of a recent murder. In fact, the well-preserved man had died 2000 years before!

Tollund man was named after the place where he was found, a bog called Tollund Fen. A bog is a very old wetland where scrubby trees and low plants grow between pools of open water. Tollund man lasted because he was buried in a bog. Why? For two reasons.

First, bog water stands still. The oxygen in it was used up long ago. Without much oxygen, most bacteria can't live. And without bacteria, many things decay very slowly.

And second, although a bog doesn't have much oxygen, it does have a lot of tannic acid. That's the same acid that's in tea. This tea-like bath takes years to brew. It's made up of decaying bog plants. The bog water soaked into Tollund man and tanned him like leather. It made him a poor meal for the few insects and bacteria that lived in the bog.

The bog protected Tollund man well, right down to his fingernails and the short beard on his face. His brain and his inner organs were whole. Scientists were even able to take what was left of his last meal from his stomach and intestines. It was probably a thin porridge made from grains and seeds.

How did Tollund man end up in the bog? Scientists know he died a violent death because he was found with a leather noose around his neck. Perhaps he was a criminal. But more likely, he was killed as a sacrifice. Two thousand years ago, many Europeans believed in a goddess of the earth. They thought that unless they sacrificed a living person to her in the middle of the winter, spring would not come, crops would be poor and all the people would suffer.

Making Things Last

What happens when you take something from the place where it's lasted for a long time? If conditions aren't right, some things can fall apart almost before your eyes. Museum conservators try to keep that from happening. They say that decay can't be stopped, but it can be slowed down.

How do conservators preserve bog bodies once they've been brought out of the bog into the air? The problem is to keep them from rotting or drying out. The earliest conservators tried smoking them like meat but that didn't work very well. Happily, modern-day conservators have found a way that does work—freeze-drying. It keeps bog bodies almost exactly as they were when they were dug up.

LIVE MUSIC

by Adèle Geras

Miss Waverley loves music. She enjoys it so much that she becomes all "pink and plump" while listening to Beethoven. Every piece of good music she hears is like a blood transfusion. But, when the music stops, she becomes pale and thin. She sounds like an ideal violin teacher, don't you think?

April 22
Moved in. I like this street. There are lots of trees and all the blossoms are out. The fronts of the houses are painted white. The doors are different colours and ours is red. There's a violin teacher living right across the road from us, so that's convenient. I'm going to go and have lessons there twice a week. She's called Miss Waverley.

April 24
Miss Waverley's windows are filthy. Mum says it's 'cos she's old and can't clean them properly, but

she seems quite healthy to me. Her garden is overgrown and there's a grave-shaped flowerbed in the front. Probably a pupil who always played out of tune, ha, ha. First lesson day after tomorrow.

April 25
Met Alan, who lives next door to Miss Waverley. He says the sawings and scrapings of her pupils come right through the wall of his lounge and sometimes drown out the television programs. In the evenings she plays gramophone records of famous violinists and Alan says it's just as bad and he can't tell the difference. Squealing and wailing, that's what he calls it. Alan is not very musical. He has lessons with Miss Waverley, too.

April 26
Had my first lesson. The inside of the house is not as bad as the windows, but Miss Waverley must be quite poor. Carpets are beige with all the flower pattern nearly trodden out of them. Walls were cream once but haven't been painted for years. Curtains are red velvet, but faded and worn. Miss Waverley is small and thin and very pale. Her eyes are blue with deep purple smudges underneath. I played Schubert. She just listened and when I'd finished she looked very happy. Her cheeks looked pink. She said I had talent. She said that teaching me would be a treat for her.

April 29
Had my second lesson. Did exercises. Played

Schubert again. Worked on it a bit. Miss Waverley listens very hard. I've never known anyone concentrate more on listening, put more effort into it.

May 3

Violin lesson this afternoon. Later, saw Miss Waverley coming back from the shops in a beige coat and a hat with cherries pinned on to it. Usually, she looks like a beetle, scuttling along in a black coat and a black straw hat. It must be the spring. She's looking altogether better. Pinker and healthier.

May 6

My phrasing and fingering are improving, I think. Miss Waverley is quite good at technique, but there's something odd and rather horrible about the way she listens. She sits back in her chair with her eyes closed and her mouth half open and gulps in the music with awful long shuddery breaths that make me feel scared. Sometimes I close my eyes while I play so as not to see her sitting there, but then my head is filled with a picture of the notes I'm playing sliding out like tiny black fish from the tip of my bow as I make them, and travelling through the air as though it were water. They swim into her mouth and are sucked along her veins, and when that happens I feel as if I haven't got them any more. I feel as if they've moved out of me and into her.

May 27

My technique is definitely getting better, but there's something wrong with my playing. Before I went to Miss Waverley, I had some control over what kind of sounds I could make. I had an idea of what the shape of the piece would be, of what the mood or the feel of it would be. Now, when I go for a lesson, I feel breathless. A sort of choking feeling from the minute I get into the room.

June 7

I told Alan about Miss Waverley. I had to. I just couldn't keep it to myself any more. I hoped he'd just laugh, but he agreed with me that there was something very strange about her. He said he'd first noticed it last Christmas. They'd taken Miss Waverley to a concert, him and his parents. Alan said that she looked half dead that night. Almost as lifeless as the three staring foxes that she wore round her neck—ugh! At the concert, during the Beethoven Violin Concerto, Miss Waverley was like a child with a lolly. That's what Alan said. He said she was lapping up the music with every bit of her body. He said that what happened to Miss Waverley at the concert is what happens to Japanese paper flowers. They start out all shrivelled and dry and you can't see what colour they are, and then the moisture puffs them out into reds and pinks and sunshine yellows. They uncurl. They blossom. They grow. And that's what happened to Miss Waverley. She became all pink and plump from listening to the music. That's what Alan said.

June 9
I always make Miss Waverley a cup of tea before we begin. Alan and I call her kitchen the Black Hole of Freemont Drive, because the rhododendrons grow right up over the windows and block out the light. She sits there listening to me play and sipping her tea and it's as if she is sipping up my music at the same time. Sip, gulp, sip.

June 12
I've noticed that when I've had my lesson, I don't feel like practising afterwards. It never used to be like that. I used to rush home from lessons and I'd hardly be inside the door before starting to practise. I also used to get up early in the morning sometimes because making the music felt so good. It feels good less and less often now.

June 15
I sometimes feel like a jug that's nearly empty. The notes I play sound thin to me, but Miss Waverley is quite pleased with my progress.

June 18
Miss Waverley smiles a lot more than she did. I've felt very tired after the last couple of lessons.

June 21
Hardly feel like playing at all now, so I don't, but it

makes me feel sad that I don't. It's as though someone had lopped off a part of me. Perhaps I would be O.K. with a different teacher. Would Mum agree?

June 25
Nearly fainted in the lesson today. Missed the last ten minutes. Told Miss Waverley I'd make the time up another day. She looked quite annoyed.

July 1
Asked Miss Waverley today had she ever taught someone famous. She said no, but some of her pupils might have become famous if they'd had a different teacher. I said something about maybe they weren't the right pupils, but she said no, they were just right, and she'd benefitted greatly from teaching them. She smiled.

July 12
Miss Waverley looks much better than she did. The smudges under her eyes have gone and her cheeks have filled out and turned all pink.

July 15
Glory be! Mum wants me to change teachers. There's a Mr. Poliansky who's very posh. You have to audition for him and he only chooses you if he thinks you're good enough. Am I still good enough? Could I be? What will Miss Waverley say? Will she be upset? I'll have to work so hard. Mum

has arranged for me to see Mr. Poliansky next week.

July 20
Hurray and three cheers, he's accepted me. I couldn't believe it. He's lovely. He looks just like a violin teacher should look—tall and thin with white wavy hair and a pointy white beard. I tried so hard when I was playing for him that I nearly fell over with the effort. It was like reaching down into a tall glass jar and trying to fish a marble out of it between your fingers. It sounded pretty awful to me, but Mr. Poliansky said my technique was very good. Technically very competent, he said, and also that he thought he detected a flicker of talent in there somewhere. Now I shall have to tell Miss Waverley. Dread, dread …

July 21
Told Miss Waverley. She was very good about it really. Quite sad, of course, and going on about what a treat it had been for her. She called it "a deeply satisfying experience." Then she said: "You've given me everything you had it in you to give," or something like that. I didn't quite understand it. Then we said goodbye to one another.

August 17
Back from holiday in Scarborough. The weather was lovely. I didn't take my violin with me this

time, although I've always taken it on holiday before. As soon as I got home, I played a bit of Mozart. It sounded very rusty and mechanical to me.

August 21
Saw Miss Waverley in her garden. Said hello. Talked about the weather. The smudges are coming back under her eyes and her face looks thinner and quite pale.

August 25
Alan says Miss Waverley is wasting away. He says she lives on good music like a vampire lives on blood. She hasn't got another pupil as good as I was, so she's getting thinner and paler. I told Alan that I felt guilty, but he said I needn't feel bad about it because she'd already taken what she could from me. I said: what has she taken? and Alan said: your talent. I stormed out of the room when he said that, but I wonder if it's true? And if it's true, then will my talent ever come back? Be brought back? What will Mr. Poliansky say? Dreading my first lesson with him.

September 1
That's over and not nearly as bad as I expected. Mr. Poliansky was quite pleased with me, I think. He made me play the same section of the Beethoven six times. I saw Miss Waverley going to the shops on my way home. She is back in her long black coat

again. Her face was quite white. Her skin looked like paper.

September 25
Miss Waverley died yesterday. Alan's mum and dad are going to the funeral. All the curtains in the street are pulled shut, for mourning. Alan thinks he was almost the last person to talk to her, if not the very last. He says he went round to her house with a plate of scones from his mother the evening before she died. They talked about me. Alan asked her if she was missing me, and she said she wasn't missing me at all because by the time I'd stopped going to her, my talent was almost completely used up. That's what Alan told me.

October 1
I've been thinking. If Miss Waverley was some kind of vampire, then why was she? What makes someone become like that? I've discussed it with Alan. We think maybe she was very talented as a child and had a teacher who sucked all the talent out of her. Then she had to use her pupils' talent to keep herself going, and in the end she needed it just to stay alive. It was like blood to her. Every bit of good music she heard was like a transfusion, and when I left and no one came to replace me, well, then she couldn't live any longer.

October 3
Have I got any talent left at all? If I have, is it

enough? Enough for me to enjoy it and be happy playing the violin? If it's not enough, or if it has all gone, then what am I going to do about it? There are only two choices: turn into another Miss Waverley, and try and exist on other people's talents, or else give up completely. I'll decide after the concert at Christmas. Mr. Poliansky isn't saying a word. He just teaches me, week in and week out, listens to me in silence and sometimes shakes his head from side to side, rather sadly.

December 17
I'm giving up the violin. I've decided. Mum will kick up a fuss but Mr. Poliansky will be on my side. I know this because I overheard him talking to someone during the concert interval last night. I know they were discussing me. Mr. Poliansky's friend said: "A very professional technique ... you must admit that."

Mr. Poliansky sighed and said: "And what use is that, eh? You tell me. For technique we have the robot music, the electronics, the synthesizers, no? Where is the heart? Where is the soul? Where, I ask you, is the *music* in that parade of so-correct notes? No, I fear she is a hopeless case. She has had the marrow and the blood sucked from the bones of the music. The sound is there but the life is gone."

"Sucked?" his friend replied. "How do you mean, sucked? Perhaps this child never had the music in her to begin with."

"But she did," Mr. Poliansky sounded sad. "Yes, I think she did. At the end of a lesson sometimes I catch a flicker of talent, like a cloud moving over water, then it's gone. Personally, I blame her previous teacher, but what can I do? I teach and teach but I cannot put the life back into the music. Come, let us go and find coffee and gather our strength for the next half."

So. There it is. Mr. Poliansky will support me. And I have the rest of my life to find something that will fill all the empty spaces in me where the music used to be.

▲▼▶▼▶▲▼▶▼▶▲▼▶▼▶▲▼▶▼▶▶

THE BOY FROM NOWHERE

by William Warren

Perhaps this story lies somewhere between
fiction and truth. Kaspar Hauser may really
have existed almost 200 years ago, but his
story will always be a mystery.

Shoemaker George Weichman looked up when
the boy entered his shop. The place was
Nuremberg, Germany; the date, May 26, 1828.

Weichman stared at the boy. Never in all his
years had he seen such a strange sight.

The boy appeared to be sixteen or seventeen
years old. His hair was long and dirty. He was
wearing ill-fitting peasant's clothes, and he seemed
to have great difficulty walking. He squinted and
blinked constantly, as if the bright sunlight outside
hurt his eyes.

"Yes? What is it?" the shoemaker asked. The
boy did not reply. His nervous manner indicated
that he was confused and afraid.

"Are you lost, boy?" Weichman asked. Still
the boy said nothing. He appeared unsteady on his

feet, and the shoemaker wondered if the boy was either drunk or retarded.

At last the boy cleared his throat. "I—I-want-to-be-a-soldier-like-my-father-was," he said in a robotlike voice. He reached into his pocket and produced a handwritten note. He gave it to Weichman, who read it carefully.

The note was unsigned, but it appeared to have been written by a man. He said that the boy had been left on his doorstep in 1812. He had ten children of his own, he said, and he had not let the boy out of his house for sixteen years. Now he asked that the boy be taken into the German army. Either that, the note said, or "If you do not want him, you can kill him."

The shoemaker looked up at the boy. "Who are you?" he asked. Again the boy did not answer him.

Thinking that the boy might be hungry, Weichman offered him meat, bread, and milk. The boy gobbled down the bread as if he had not eaten in a long time. He also drank some water, but he acted as if he had never seen milk or meat before.

When the boy had finished eating, Weichman took him to the police station. There, the boy pointed to his chest and said, "Kaspar-Hauser." Then he repeated his singsong statement that he wanted to be a soldier as his father had been. The policemen questioned Kaspar thoroughly, but his only other reply was a dull "I-don't-know." They concluded that he must be retarded.

What they didn't know at the time was that those few words in German were virtually the only ones that Kaspar knew.

The policemen found a second note in Kaspar's clothes. It was also handwritten. This time the writer claimed to be his mother. She said that his name was Kaspar and he had been baptized; his father, an ex-soldier, was dead; and she was too poor to take care of Kaspar. The officers concluded that both notes were fake. But Kaspar could not have written them: he didn't know how to write.

One of the policemen took Kaspar home with him. Before long, he discovered exactly how strange a boy Kaspar Hauser was.

At first, when Kaspar walked he looked like a baby taking its first awkward steps. He stumbled over objects in his path rather than walking around them. The soles of his feet were tender and thin-skinned, indicating that he had never walked much, if at all.

Other aspects of Kaspar's behaviour were equally unusual and mysterious.

When he entered the policeman's house for the first time, he tried to grasp the flame of a candle apparently because he thought it was pretty. It burned his hand. He was frightened by moonlight and loud noises. And during his first few days in the policeman's house, foods other than bread and water made him sick.

Kaspar's vision was perfect, but he seemed to be severely colourblind—as if he had spent much of his life in darkness. Indeed, bright lights hurt his eyes, and he could see in the dark like an animal. His sense of smell was much keener than the average human's. Strangest of all, Kaspar could even see stars in the sky during the daytime as well as at night.

As word of the strange boy began to spread throughout Germany, he attracted the attention of a Professor Daumer who agreed to work with Kaspar. He began teaching Kaspar, and found him to be intelligent and a quick learner. Soon, Kaspar was able to tell the professor what his earlier life had been like. And like practically everything else about the boy, his story was astonishing.

Before his arrival in Nuremberg (Kaspar said), he spent his entire life in a small cell that was about two metres long, one metre wide, and no more than one and a half metres high. His only companion was a wooden toy soldier. He slept on a bed of straw in his unlighted cell, and he never had seen another human until the day a man brought him to Nuremberg.

Each morning when he awoke, he found fresh bread and water in his cell. Sometimes, the water tasted bad and he fell asleep after drinking it. When he awoke, he'd find that he had been washed, his hair and nails trimmed, and his cell cleaned while he was asleep.

One day, Kaspar said, a man entered his cell. The man taught him to say a few words—"Kaspar Hauser," "I don't know," and "I want to be a soldier like my father was"—and carried him outside his underground cell for the first time in his life. The bright sunlight made him dizzy, and he fainted. When he awoke, he was lying outside the shoemaker's shop in Nuremberg.

Meanwhile, the police were still trying to find out who the boy named "Kaspar Hauser" really was. Posters bearing his likeness were spread throughout Germany and the rest of Europe with little success. Everyone was interested in the case, but no one seemed to know anything about the boy.

A man came forward to announce that he had found a bottle with a message inside it. The note was a plea for help from someone who said he was being held prisoner in a cell on the banks of the Rhine River. The note was signed *Hares Sprauka* which, the police noted, was "Kaspar Hauser" with the letters rearranged. But Kaspar said that he had written no such note—in all his years living in a cell, he didn't know that he was a prisoner because he had no idea what life was like outside the cell. Besides, he pointed out, he didn't even know how to write at the time.

The police made a thorough search along the banks of the Rhine, but they found no such prisoner or cell.

In October, 1829, Kaspar was attacked and left unconscious and bleeding in the policeman's home by a man wielding a club. Kaspar did not see his attacker's face, and he had no idea why he was assaulted.

The man, who had worn a mask, was never identified or caught. All the police knew for sure was that the man had not been a burglar: except for the cellar where Kaspar was attacked, the house was undisturbed. No money, jewelry, silverware, or other valuables were missing.

During the next four years, Kaspar lived with several different guardians. The last of his guardians was an Englishman, Lord Charles Stanhope. Lord Stanhope took Kaspar to live in his home in Ansbach, Bavaria.

On December 14, 1833, Kaspar received a note asking him to meet someone in a public park in Ansbach. If he did so, the note explained, he would find out who his mother and father were.

At the park, Kaspar met a man he later described as having a thick beard and moustache and wearing a long, dark coat.

"Are you Kaspar Hauser?" the man asked. Kaspar replied that he was. The man offered him a purse, but as he accepted it the man stabbed him in his side and ran away. The wound was severe but Kaspar somehow managed to get home before he collapsed, bleeding and in shock. He died three days later.

The police investigated the case. They found the purse lying in the snow, but no murder weapon was ever found. They discovered, too, that the only footprints leading to and from the purse belonged to Kaspar Hauser. But before he died, Kaspar told the police that he had not stabbed himself. He could not identify his attacker.

Kaspar was buried in Ansbach cemetery. On the tombstone over his grave are these words: "Here lies Kaspar Hauser, an enigma of his time, of unknown birth, of peculiar death, 1833."

Was Kaspar Hauser Telling the Truth?

Even if we would like to believe Kaspar Hauser's weird tale of being imprisoned alone in a tiny cell as far back as he could remember, his story does not ring true. It just doesn't sound right. After all, is it possible that he never once saw another human being before the man suddenly appeared one day to teach him a few words and take him to Nuremberg?

Kaspar was sixteen or seventeen years old when he showed up at the shoemaker's shop. He must have undergone periods of illness in his earlier years: times when he needed medical or dental treatment, or times when he ran a high fever and needed constant, close attention. How could he have received such treatment without at least once accidentally seeing someone? Even if we assume that he was given knock-out drugs in his food whenever other humans needed to approach him, he could not have survived being given such powerful drugs when he was running a high fever.

Other questions are equally baffling. For instance, how was his cell heated and cooled? He said that his cell was located deep underground; if it was not heated or cooled to allow for changes in the seasons, he must have been sick much of the time, which leads us back to the previous questions about his health. And if his cell was artificially heated, he could not have failed to see someone adjusting the heat in some manner during his sixteen years of confinement.

Finally, if, as he said, he had been deprived of contact with other humans all his life, he should have been severely unstable emotionally. Studies involving animals who are kept away from other animals from birth have shown that they quickly develop signs of extreme mental illness. Even when they are allowed to mingle with other animals later, they never overcome the mental problems that developed early in their lives. Yet no such evidence exists that Kaspar Hauser was mentally ill or unable to live a normal life around other people.

On the other hand, why would he lie about his past? And more importantly, *could* he have lied about it? It seems hardly possible that he could have faked all of his physical problems and talents—inability to walk, seeing in the dark, sunlight hurting his eyes, his keen sense of smell, throwing up whenever he had food other than bread and water, and so forth.

But even these problems seem unimportant when compared to the most important question of all.

Where Did Kaspar Hauser Come From?

No one ever found out where the boy came from. He showed up one day in May, 1828; he was stabbed to death in December, 1833. And to this day, his true origin is still a mystery.

The story of Kaspar Hauser was well known throughout Europe. Several theories were offered as to his true identity and where he came from.

According to one such theory, Kaspar was the secret son of an innkeeper's daughter and a priest. Another theory had him coming to earth from another planet, set down among us so the alien creatures could study the way humans reacted to him.

By far the most popular theory at the time was that Kaspar was the son of Grand Duke Karl Frederick and Grand Duchess Stephanie, the ruling family of Baden.

Immediately after his birth (or so the rumour went), Kaspar was kidnapped and taken from the Duke's palace. He was replaced by a dead baby. (The duke had no children; without a direct heir his throne would pass to another branch of his family when he died.) Meanwhile, young Kaspar secretly was taken to live with an ex-soldier who was in league with the kidnappers. Years later, when the boy grew too large to remain in the cell (or when the ex-soldier grew tired of keeping him), the world got its first glimpse of Kaspar Hauser.

And if you accept this latter version of Kaspar's origin, you'll probably decide that the two attempts to kill him were made because he was the rightful heir to the throne of Baden.

You may be right, too.

Kaspar Hauser was said to bear a strong resemblance to the duke and duchess. If so, he may have been murdered because his continued existence was seen as a threat to the man who succeeded to the throne when the grand duke died in 1830. (It is interesting that the Earl of Stanhope—Kaspar's final legal guardian who took him to live in Ansbach, Bavaria, where he was murdered in 1833—was a close friend of the man who eventually inherited the throne.)

But we'll probably never know for sure who Kaspar Hauser really was, or why he was murdered. And that's why even now, more than 150 years after his mysterious life and death, the story of Kaspar Hauser remains one of the most fascinating unexplained mysteries in Europe's long and colourful history.

▲▼▼▲▼▶▼▲▼▶▼▲▼▶▼▲▼▶▼▲▶▶

THE SUMMER OF THE
BEAUTIFUL WHITE HORSE

by William Saroyan

One wonderful summer, Aram and Mourad
galloped into the morning on the horse of
their dreams. There was just one problem. It
wasn't their horse.

One day back there in the good old days when I
was nine and the world was full of every
imaginable kind of magnificence, and life was still
a delightful and mysterious dream, my cousin
Mourad, who was considered crazy by everybody
who knew him except me, came to my house at
four in the morning and woke me up by tapping on
the window of my room.

Aram, he said.

I jumped out of bed and looked out the
window.

I couldn't believe what I saw.

It wasn't morning yet, but it was summer and
with daybreak not many minutes around the
corner of the world it was light enough for me to

know I wasn't dreaming.

My cousin Mourad was sitting on a beautiful white horse.

I stuck my head out of the window and rubbed my eyes.

Yes, he said in Armenian. It's a horse. You're not dreaming. Make it quick if you want to ride.

I knew my cousin Mourad enjoyed being alive more than anybody else who had ever fallen into the world by mistake, but this was more than even I could believe.

In the first place, my earliest memories had been memories of horses and my first longings had been longings to ride.

This was the wonderful part.

In the second place, we were poor.

This was the part that wouldn't permit me to believe what I saw.

We were poor. We had no money. Our whole tribe was poverty-stricken. Every branch of the Garoghlanian family was living in the most amazing and comical poverty in the world. Nobody could understand where we ever got money enough to keep us with food in our bellies, not even the old men of the family. Most important of all, though, we were famous for our honesty. We had been famous for our honesty for something like eleven centuries, even when we had been the wealthiest family in what we liked to think was the world. We were proud first, honest next, and after that we believed in right and wrong. None of us would take advantage of anybody in the world, let alone steal.

Consequently, even though I could *see* the horse, so magnificent; even though I could *smell* it, so lovely; even though I could *hear* it breathing, so exciting; I couldn't *believe* the horse had anything to do with my cousin Mourad or with me or with any of the other members of our family, asleep or awake, because I *knew* my cousin Mourad couldn't have *bought* the horse, and if he couldn't have bought it he must have *stolen* it, and I refused to believe he had stolen it.

No member of the Garoghlanian family could be a thief.

I stared first at my cousin and then at the horse. There was a pious stillness and humour in each of them which on the one hand delighted me and on the other frightened me.

Mourad, I said, where did you steal this horse?

Leap out of the window, he said, if you want to ride.

It was true, then. He *had* stolen the horse. There was no question about it. He had come to invite me to ride or not, as I chose.

Well, it seemed to me stealing a horse for a ride was not the same thing as stealing something else, such as money. For all I knew, maybe it wasn't stealing at all. If you were crazy about horses the way my cousin Mourad and I were, it wasn't stealing. It wouldn't become stealing until we offered to sell the horse, which of course I knew we would never do.

Let me put on some clothes, I said.

All right, he said, but hurry.

I leaped into my clothes.

I jumped down to the yard from the window and leaped up onto the horse behind my cousin Mourad.

That year we lived at the edge of town, on Walnut Avenue. Behind our house was the country: vineyards, orchards, irrigation ditches, and country roads. In less than three minutes we were on Olive Avenue, and then the horse began to trot. The air was new and lovely to breathe. The feel of the horse running was wonderful. My cousin Mourad who was considered one of the craziest members of our family began to sing. I mean, he began to roar.

Every family has a crazy streak in it somewhere, and my cousin Mourad was considered the natural descendant of the crazy streak in our tribe. Before him was our uncle Khosrove, an enormous man with a powerful head of black hair and the largest moustache in the San Joaquin Valley, a man so furious in temper, so irritable, so impatient that he stopped anyone from talking by roaring, *It is no harm; pay no attention to it.*

That was all, no matter what anybody happened to be talking about. Once it was his own son Arak running eight blocks to the barber shop where his father was having his moustache trimmed to tell him their house was on fire. This man Khosrove sat up in the chair and roared, It is no harm; pay no attention to it. The barber said, But the boy says your house is on fire. So Khosrove roared, Enough, it is no harm, I say.

My cousin Mourad was considered the natural descendant of this man, although Mourad's father was Zorab, who was practical and nothing else. That's how it was in our tribe. A man could be the father of his son's flesh, but that did not mean that he was also the father of his spirit. The distribution of the various kinds of spirit of our tribe had been from the beginning capricious and vagrant.

We rode and my cousin Mourad sang. For all anybody knew we were still in the old country where, at least according to some of our neighbours, we belonged. We let the horse run as long as it felt like running.

At last my cousin Mourad said, Get down. I want to ride alone.

Will you let me ride alone? I said.

That is up to the horse, my cousin said. Get down.

The *horse* will let me ride, I said.

We shall see, he said. Don't forget that I have a way with a horse.

Well, I said, any way you have with a horse, I have also.

For the sake of your safety, he said, let us

hope so. Get down.

All right, I said, but remember you've got to let me try to ride alone.

I got down and my cousin Mourad kicked his heels into the horse and shouted, *Vazire*, run. The horse stood on its hind legs, snorted, and burst into a fury of speed that was the loveliest thing I had ever seen. My cousin Mourad raced the horse across a field of dry grass to an irrigation ditch, crossed the ditch on the horse, and five minutes later returned, dripping wet.

The sun was coming up.

Now it's my turn to ride, I said.

My cousin Mourad got off the horse.

Ride, he said.

I leaped to the back of the horse and for a moment knew the awfulest fear imaginable. The horse did not move.

Kick into his muscles, my cousin Mourad said. What are you waiting for? We've got to take him back before everybody in the world is up and about.

I kicked into the muscles of the horse. Once again it reared and snorted. Then it began to run. I didn't know what to do. Instead of running across the field to the irrigation ditch the horse ran down the road to the vineyard of Dikran Halabian where it began to leap over vines. The horse leaped over seven vines before I fell. Then it continued running.

My cousin Mourad came running down the road.

I'm not worried about you, he shouted. We've got to get that horse. You go this way and I'll go this way. If you come upon him, be kindly. I'll be near.

I continued down the road and my cousin Mourad went across the field toward the irrigation ditch.

It took him half an hour to find the horse and bring him back.

All right, he said, jump on. The whole world is awake now.

What will we do? I said.

Well, he said, we'll either take him back or hide him until tomorrow morning.

He didn't sound worried and I knew he'd hide him and not take him back. Not for a while, at any rate.

Where will we hide him? I said.

I know a place, he said.

How long ago did you steal this horse? I said.

It suddenly dawned on me that he had been taking these early morning rides for some time and had come for me this morning only because he knew how much I longed to ride.

Who said anything about stealing a horse? he said.

Anyhow, I said, how long ago did you begin riding every morning?

Not until this morning, he said.

Are you telling the truth? I said.

Of course not, he said, but if we are found

out, that's what you're to say. I don't want both of us to be liars. All you know is that we started riding this morning.

All right, I said.

He walked the horse quietly to the barn of a deserted vineyard which at one time had been the pride of a farmer named Fetvajian. There were some oats and dry alfalfa in the barn.

We began walking home.

It wasn't easy, he said, to get the horse to behave so nicely. At first it wanted to run wild, but, as I've told you, I have a way with a horse. I can get it to want to do anything I want it to do. Horses understand me.

How do you do it? I said.

I have an understanding with a horse, he said.

Yes, but what sort of an understanding? I said.

A simple and honest one, he said.

Well, I said, I wish I knew how to reach an understanding like that with a horse.

You're still a small boy, he said. When you get to be thirteen you'll know how to do it.

I went home and ate a hearty breakfast.

That afternoon my uncle Khosrove came to our house for coffee and cigarettes. He sat in the parlour, sipping and smoking and remembering the old country. Then another visitor arrived, a farmer named John Byro, an Assyrian who, out of loneliness, had learned to speak Armenian. My mother brought the lonely visitor coffee and tobacco and he rolled a cigarette and sipped and smoked, and then at last, sighing sadly, he said, My white horse which was stolen last month is still gone. I cannot understand it.

My uncle Khosrove became very irritated and shouted, It's no harm. What is the loss of a horse? Haven't we all lost the homeland? What is this crying over a horse?

That may be all right for you, a city dweller, to say, John Byro said, but what of my surrey? What good is a surrey without a horse?

Pay no attention to it, my uncle Khosrove roared.

I walked ten miles to get here, John Byro said.

You have legs, my uncle Khosrove shouted.

My left leg pains me, the farmer said.

Pay no attention to it, my uncle Khosrove roared.

That horse cost me sixty dollars, the farmer said.

I spit on money, my uncle Khosrove said.

He got up and stalked out of the house, slamming the screen door.

My mother explained.

He has a gentle heart, she said. It is simply that he is homesick and such a large man.

The farmer went away and I ran over to my cousin Mourad's house.

He was sitting under a peach tree, trying to repair the hurt wing of a young robin which could not fly. He was talking to the bird.

What is it? he said.

The farmer John Byro, I said. He visited our house. He wants his horse. You've had it a month. I want you to promise not to take it back until I learn to ride.

It will take you *a year* to learn to ride, my cousin Mourad said.

We could keep the horse a year, I said.

My cousin Mourad leaped to his feet.

What? he roared. Are you inviting a member of the Garoghlanian family to steal? The horse must go back to its true owner.

When? I said.

In six months at the latest, he said.

He threw the bird into the air. The bird tried hard, almost fell twice, but at last flew away, high and straight.

Early every morning for two weeks my cousin Mourad and I took the horse out of the barn of the deserted vineyard where we were hiding it and rode it, and every morning the horse, when it was my turn to ride alone, leaped over grape vines and small trees and threw me and ran away. Nevertheless, I hoped in time to learn to ride the way my cousin Mourad rode.

One morning on the way to Fetvajian's deserted vineyard we ran into the farmer John Byro who was on his way to town.

Let me do the talking, my cousin Mourad said. I have a way with farmers.

Good morning, John Byro, my cousin Mourad

said to the farmer.

The farmer studied the horse eagerly.

Good morning, sons of my friends, he said. What is the name of your horse?

My Heart, my cousin Mourad said in Armenian.

A lovely name, John Byro said, for a lovely horse. I could swear it is the horse that was stolen from me many weeks ago. May I look into its mouth?

Of course, Mourad said.

The farmer looked into the mouth of the horse.

Tooth for tooth, he said. I would swear it *is* my horse if I didn't know your parents. The fame of your family for honesty is well known to me. Yet the horse is the twin of my horse. A suspicious man would believe his eyes instead of his heart. Good day, my young friends.

Good day, John Byro, my cousin Mourad said.

Early the following morning we took the horse to John Byro's vineyard and put it in the barn. The dogs followed us around without making a sound.

The dogs, I whispered to my cousin Mourad. I thought they would bark.

They would at somebody else, he said. I have a way with dogs.

My cousin Mourad put his arms around the horse, pressed his nose into the horse's nose, patted it, and then we went away.

That afternoon John Byro came to our house in his surrey and showed my mother the horse that had been stolen and returned.

I do not know what to think, he said. The horse is stronger than ever. Better-tempered, too. I thank God.

My uncle Khosrove, who was in the parlour, became irritated and shouted, Quiet, man, quiet. Your horse has been returned. Pay no attention to it.

MIDNIGHT

The graveyard is silent.
The howling wind rushes by.
I hear a noise and spin around,
around and around.
There it is again; tap, tap, tap.
Looking behind a gravestone,
I see a vision of a man
With a hammer and chisel.
I ask him what he is doing,
He replies, "They spelt my name wrong."

Baljit Kang

Justice
With a Twist

▲ ▼ ▶ ▼ ▲ ▼ ▶ ▼ ▶ ▲ ▼ ▶ ▼ ▲ ▼ ▶ ▼ ▶ ▶

My Aunt

You've heard how a green thumb
Makes flowers come
Quite without toil
Out of any old soil.

Well, my Aunt's thumbs were green.
At a touch, she had blooms
Of prize Chrysanthemums—
The grandest ever seen.

People from miles around
Came to see those flowers
And were truly astounded
By her unusual powers.

One day a little weed
Pushed up to drink and feed
Among the pampered flowers
At her water-can showers.

Day by day it grew
With ragged leaves and bristles
Till it was tall as me or you—
It was a King of Thistles.

"Prizes for flowers are easy,"
My Aunt said in her pride.
"But was there ever such a weed
The whole world wide?"

She watered it, she tended it,
It grew alarmingly.
As if I had offended it,
It bristled over me.

"Oh Aunt!" I cried. "Beware of that!
I saw it eat a bird."
She went on polishing its points
As if she hadn't heard.

"Oh Aunt!" I cried. "It has a flower
Like a lion's beard—"
Too late! It was devouring her
Just as I had feared!

Her feet were waving in the air—
But I shall not proceed.
Here ends the story of my Aunt
And her ungrateful weed.

Ted Hughes

▲ ▼ ▶ ▼ ▶ ▲ ▼ ▶ ▼ ▶ ▲ ▼ ▶ ▼ ▶ ▲ ▼ ▶ ▼ ▶

TWO STORIES TO SOLVE

by George Shannon

This is your chance to match wits with clever
folks from long ago and far away! Give it your
best shot before you check the answers at the
ends of the stories.

OUTWITTING THE KING

In ancient Ethiopia the men studying to be
priests and village teachers were among the
poorest and the cleverest. They were not allowed to
own anything and so lived by their wits as they
travelled around the country to study with monks.

Once a king decided he would catch not only
every thief in his country but every potential thief
as well. Knowing that the men studying to be
village teachers were always in need of money, the
king called them all to the palace. His plan was to
scatter gold coins in the courtyard. The next
morning, when the students passed through, he
would arrest anyone who picked up a coin. The
coins were scattered, and the students passed

through the courtyard. No one bent down to pick up a coin, yet all the coins were gone when the students left.

Determined to catch the one who had taken the coins, the king invited all the students to a banquet and to spend the night. There was lots of food and wine, and the king's spies were everywhere. If any of the spies heard a student bragging about stealing the coins, he was to make a secret mark on that student's arm while he slept. Then, when the students left the next morning, the king would look at their arms as they passed by and grab the thief himself.

One of the spies did hear a student boast how he'd picked up the gold coins by rubbing wax on the bottom of his shoes, and the spy made the secret mark on that student's arm. The next morning, as they all walked past, the king saw the secret mark, but he still could not figure out who had taken the coins. Why?

How It Was Done

When the student woke and saw the mark, he had put identical marks on their arms.

THE BET

In the old South when people claimed they could own other people, there lived a slave, named John, who could outsmart anybody for miles around. He was always making bets, and he never made a bet he didn't win. This only made people more eager to bet with him. Everyone, including Colonel Blake, wanted to say that he'd been the first to outsmart John.

"I'll bet you," John said to him one day, "that I can stand at one end of your parlour and throw a raw egg all the way across the room and onto the fireplace mantel without breaking the egg. I'll bet you fifty dollars, all the money I have."

The colonel quickly agreed to the bet. He was certain nobody could throw a raw egg without having it break.

"I'll even give you a dozen tries," he told John.

The first egg John threw smashed on the edge of the mantel. The second hit the candlestick sitting on top. The third egg smashed and smeared the painting above the mantel, but the colonel just laughed. He was happy because he was going to be able to say he was the first to outsmart John on a bet. John threw all twelve eggs, but not one landed without breaking.

"Looks as if I won the bet," said Colonel Blake with a bragging smile.

"Yes," said John. "Sure looks that way."

He paid him the fifty dollars, but when John went to bed that night, he still had fifty dollars from winning a bet. Where did it come from?

How It Was Done

John had also made a bet for a hundred dollars with the neighbouring plantation owner. He bet he could throw eggs all over Colonel Blake's parlour and that the colonel would only watch and laugh. By losing the first bet on purpose, John had managed to outsmart both men at the same time.

LAMB TO THE SLAUGHTER

by Roald Dahl

Mary Maloney was quite content as she waited for her detective husband to come home for dinner. Such a shock, when he came home with bad news! But she acted quickly.

The room was warm and clean, the curtains drawn, the two table lamps alight—hers and the one by the empty chair opposite. On the sideboard behind her, two tall glasses, soda water, whiskey. Fresh ice cubes in the Thermos bucket.

Mary Maloney was waiting for her husband to come home from work.

Now and again she would glance up at the clock, but without anxiety, merely to please herself with the thought that each minute gone by made it nearer the time when he would come. There was a slow smiling air about her, and about everything she did. The drop of the head as she bent over her sewing was curiously tranquil. Her skin—for this was her sixth month with child—had acquired a wonderful translucent quality, the mouth was soft, and the eyes, with their new placid look, seemed larger, darker than before.

When the clock said ten minutes to five, she began to listen, and a few moments later, punctually as always, she heard the tires on the gravel outside, and the car door slamming, the footsteps passing the window, the key turning in the lock. She laid aside her sewing, stood up, and went forward to kiss him as he came in.

"Hullo darling," she said.

"Hullo," he answered.

She took his coat and hung it in the closet. Then she walked over and made the drinks, a strongish one for him, a weak one for herself; and soon she was back again in her chair with the sewing, and he in the other, opposite, holding the tall glass with both his hands, rocking it so the ice cubes tinkled against the side.

For her, this was always a blissful time of day. She knew he didn't want to speak much until the first drink was finished, and she, on her side, was content to sit quietly, enjoying his company after the long hours alone in the house. She loved to luxuriate in the presence of this man, and to feel— almost as a sunbather feels the sun—that warm male glow that came out of him to her when they were alone together. She loved him for the way he sat loosely in a chair, for the way he came in a door, or moved slowly across the room with long strides. She loved the intent, far look in his eyes when they rested on her, the funny shape of the mouth, and especially the way he remained silent about his tiredness, sitting still with himself until the whiskey had taken some of it away.

"Tired, darling?"

"Yes," he said. "I'm tired." And as he spoke, he did an unusual thing. He lifted his glass and drained it in one swallow although there was still half of it, at least half of it left. She wasn't really watching him, but she knew what he had done because she heard the ice cubes falling back against the bottom of the empty glass when he lowered his arm. He paused a moment, leaning forward in the chair, then he got up and went slowly over to fetch himself another.

"I'll get it!" she cried, jumping up.

"Sit down," he said.

When he came back, she noticed that the new drink was dark amber with the quantity of whiskey in it.

"Darling, shall I get your slippers?"

"No."

She watched him as he began to sip the dark yellow drink, and she could see little oily swirls in the liquid because it was so strong.

"I think it's a shame," she said, "that when a policeman gets to be as senior as you, they keep him walking about on his feet all day long."

He didn't answer, so she bent her head again and went on with her sewing; but each time he lifted the drink to his lips, she heard the ice cubes clinking against the side of the glass.

"Darling," she said. "Would you like me to get you some cheese? I haven't made any supper because it's Thursday."

"No," he said.

"If you're too tired to eat out," she went on, "it's still not too late. There's plenty of meat and stuff in the freezer, and you can have it right here and not even move out of the chair."

Her eyes waited on him for an answer, a smile, a little nod, but he made no sign.

"Anyway," she went on, "I'll get you some cheese and crackers first."

"I don't want it," he said.

She moved uneasily in her chair, the large eyes still watching his face. "But you *must* have supper. I can easily do it here. I'd like to do it. We can have lamb chops. Or pork. Anything you want. Everything's in the freezer."

"Forget it," he said.

"But darling, you *must* eat! I'll fix it anyway, and then you can have it or not, as you like."

She stood up and placed her sewing on the table by the lamp.

"Sit down," he said. "Just for a minute, sit down."

It wasn't till then that she began to get frightened.

"Go on," he said. "Sit down."

She lowered herself back slowly into the chair, watching him all the time with those large, bewildered eyes. He had finished the second drink and was staring down into the glass, frowning.

"Listen," he said. "I've got something to tell you."

"What is it, darling? What's the matter?"

He had now become absolutely motionless, and he kept his head down so that the light from the lamp beside him fell across the upper part of his face, leaving the chin and mouth in shadow. She noticed there was a little muscle moving near the corner of his left eye.

"This is going to be a bit of a shock to you, I'm afraid," he said. "But I've thought about it a good deal and I've decided the only thing to do is tell you right away. I hope you won't blame me too much."

And he told her. It didn't take long, four or five minutes at most, and she sat very still through it all, watching him with a kind of dazed horror as he went further and further away from her with each word.

"So there it is," he added. "And I know it's kind of a bad time to be telling you, but there simply wasn't any other way. Of course I'll give you money and see you're looked after. But there needn't really be any fuss. I hope not anyway. It wouldn't be very good for my job."

Her first instinct was not to believe any of it, to reject it all. It occurred to her that perhaps he hadn't even spoken, that she herself had imagined the whole thing. Maybe, if she went about her business and acted as though she hadn't been listening, then later, when she sort of woke up again, she might find none of it had ever happened.

"I'll get the supper," she managed to whisper, and this time he didn't stop her.

When she walked across the room, she couldn't feel her feet touching the floor. She couldn't feel anything at all—except a slight nausea and a desire to vomit. Everything was automatic now—down the steps to the cellar, the light switch, the deep freeze, the hand inside the cabinet taking hold of the first object it met. She lifted it out and looked at it. It was wrapped in paper, so she took off the paper and looked at it again.

A leg of lamb.

All right then, they would have lamb for supper. She carried it upstairs, holding the thin bone-end of it with both her hands, and as she went through the living room, she saw him standing over by the window with his back to her, and she stopped.

"For God's sake," he said, hearing her, but not turning around. "Don't make supper for me. I'm going out."

At that point, Mary Maloney simply walked up behind him and without any pause she swung the big frozen leg of lamb high in the air and brought it down as hard as she could on the back of his head.

She might just as well have hit him with a steel club.

She stepped back a pace, waiting, and the funny thing was that he remained standing there for at least four or five seconds, gently swaying. Then he crashed to the carpet.

The violence of the crash, the noise, the small table overturning, helped bring her out of the shock. She came out slowly, feeling cold and surprised, and she stood for a while blinking at the body, still holding the ridiculous piece of meat tight with both hands.

All right, she told herself. So I've killed him.

It was extraordinary, now, how clear her mind became all of a sudden. She began thinking very fast. As the wife of a detective, she knew quite well what the penalty would be. That was fine. It made no difference to her. In fact, it would be a relief. On the other hand, what about the child? What were the laws about murderers with unborn children? Did they kill them both—mother and child? Or did they wait until the tenth month? What did they do?

Mary Maloney didn't know. And she certainly wasn't prepared to take a chance.

She carried the meat into the kitchen, placed it in a pan, turned the oven on high, and shoved it inside. Then she washed her hands and ran upstairs to the bedroom. She sat down before the mirror, tidied her hair, touched up her lips and face. She tried to smile. It came out rather peculiar. She tried again.

"Hullo Sam," she said brightly, aloud.

The voice sounded peculiar too.

"I want some potatoes please, Sam. Yes, and I think a can of peas."

That was better. Both the smile and the voice were coming out better now. She rehearsed it several times more. Then she ran downstairs, to her coat, went out the back door, down the garden, into the street.

It wasn't six o'clock yet and the lights were still on in the grocery shop.

"Hullo Sam," she said brightly, smiling at the man behind the counter.

"Why, good evening, Mrs. Maloney. How're *you*?"

"I want some potatoes please, Sam. Yes, and I think a can of peas."

The man turned and reached up behind him on the shelf for the peas.

"Patrick's decided he's tired and doesn't want to eat out tonight," she told him. "We usually go out Thursdays, you know, and now he's caught me without any vegetables in the house."

"Then how about meat, Mrs. Maloney?"

"No, I've got meat, thanks. I got a nice leg of lamb from the freezer."

"Oh."

"I don't much like cooking it frozen, Sam, but I'm taking a chance on it this time. You think it'll be all right?"

"Personally," the grocer said, "I don't believe it makes any difference. You want these Idaho potatoes?"

"Oh yes, that'll be fine. Two of th

"Anything else?" The grocer cock
on one side, looking at her pleasantly. " ow about
afterwards? What you going to give him for
afterwards?"

"Well—what would you suggest, Sam?"

The man glanced around his shop. "How
about a nice big slice of cheesecake? I know he likes
that."

"Perfect," she said. "He loves it."

And when it was all wrapped and she had
paid, she put on her brightest smile and said,
"Thank you, Sam. Good night."

"Good night, Mrs. Maloney. And thank *you*."

And now, she told herself as she hurried back,
all she was doing now, she was returning home to
her husband and he was waiting for his supper;
and she must cook it good, and make it as tasty as
possible because the poor man was tired; and if,
when she entered the house, she happened to find
anything unusual, or tragic, or terrible, then
naturally it would be a shock and she'd become
frantic with grief and horror. Mind you, she wasn't
expecting to find anything. She was just going home
with the vegetables on Thursday evening to cook
supper for her husband.

That's the way, she told herself. Do
everything right and natural. Keep things
absolutely natural, and there'll be no need for any
acting at all.

Therefore, when she entered the kitchen by the back door, she was humming a little tune to herself and smiling.

"Patrick!" she called. "How are you, darling?"

She put the parcel down on the table and went through into the living room; and when she saw him lying there on the floor with his legs doubled up and one arm twisted back underneath his body, it really was rather a shock. All the old love and longing for him welled up inside her, and she ran over to him, knelt down beside him, and began to cry her heart out. It was easy. No acting was necessary.

A few minutes later she got up and went to the phone. She knew the number of the police station, and when the man at the other end answered, she cried to him, "Quick! Come quick! Patrick's dead!"

"Who's speaking?"

"Mrs. Maloney. Mrs. Patrick Maloney."

"You mean Patrick Maloney's dead?"

"I think so," she sobbed. "He's lying on the floor and I think he's dead."

"Be right over," the man said.

The car came very quickly, and when she opened the front door, two policemen walked in. She knew them both—she knew nearly all the men at that precinct—and she fell right into Jack Noonan's arms, weeping hysterically. He put her gently into a chair, then went over to join the other one, who was called O'Malley, kneeling by the body.

"Is he dead?" she cried.

"I'm afraid he is. What happened?"

Briefly, she told her story about going out to the grocer and coming back to find him on the floor. While she was talking, crying and talking, Noonan discovered a small patch of congealed blood on the dead man's head. He showed it to O'Malley, who got up at once and hurried to the phone.

Soon, other men began to come into the house. First a doctor, then two detectives, one of whom she knew by name. Later, a police photographer arrived and took pictures, and a man who knew about fingerprints. There was a great deal of whispering and muttering beside the corpse, and the detectives kept asking her a lot of questions. But they always treated her kindly. She told her story again, this time right from the beginning, when Patrick had come in, and she was sewing, and he was tired, so tired he hadn't wanted to go out for supper. She told how she'd put the meat in the oven—"It's there now, cooking"—and how she'd slipped out to the grocer for vegetables, and come back to find him lying on the floor.

"Which grocer?" one of the detectives asked.

She told him, and he turned and whispered something to the other detective, who immediately went outside into the street.

In fifteen minutes he was back with a page of notes, and there was more whispering, and through her sobbing she heard a few of the whispered phrases—"...acted quite normal ... very cheerful ... wanted to give him a good supper ... peas ... cheesecake ... impossible that she ..."

After a while, the photographer and the doctor departed, and two other men came in and took the corpse away on a stretcher. Then the fingerprint man went away. The two detectives remained, and so did the two policemen. They were exceptionally nice to her, and Jack Noonan asked if she wouldn't rather go somewhere else, to her sister's house perhaps, or to his own wife, who would take care of her and put her up for the night.

No, she said. She didn't feel she could move even a yard at the moment. Would they mind awfully if she stayed just where she was until she felt better? She didn't feel too good at the moment, she really didn't.

Then hadn't she better lie down on the bed? Jack Noonan asked.

No, she said. She'd like to stay right where she was, in this chair. A little later perhaps, when she felt better, she would move.

So they left her there while they went about their business, searching the house. Occasionally one of the detectives asked her another question. Sometimes Jack Noonan spoke to her gently as he passed by. Her husband, he told her, had been killed by a blow on the back of the head administered with a heavy blunt instrument, almost certainly a large piece of metal. They were looking for the weapon. The murderer may have taken it with him, but on the other hand he may've thrown it away or hidden it somewhere on the premises.

"It's the old story," he said. "Get the weapon, and you've got the man."

Later, one of the detectives came up and sat beside her. Did she know, he asked, of anything in the house that could've been used as the weapon? Would she mind having a look around to see if anything was missing—a very big wrench, for example, or a heavy metal vase.

They didn't have any heavy metal vases, she said.

"Or a big wrench?"

She didn't think they had a big wrench. But there might be some things like that in the garage.

The search went on. She knew that there were other policemen in the garden all around the house. She could hear their footsteps on the gravel outside, and sometimes she saw the flash of a torch-light through a chink in the curtains. It began to get late, nearly nine she noticed by the clock on the mantel. The four men searching the rooms seemed to be growing weary, a trifle exasperated.

"Jack," she said, the next time Sergeant Noonan went by. "Would you mind giving me a drink?"

"Sure I'll give you a drink. You mean this whiskey?"

"Yes please. But just a small one. It might

make me feel better." He handed her the glass.

"Why don't you have one yourself?" she said. "You must be awfully tired. Please do. You've been very good to me."

"Well," he answered. "It's not strictly allowed, but I might take just a drop to keep me going."

One by one, the others came in and were persuaded to take a little nip of whiskey. They stood around rather awkwardly with the drinks in their hands, uncomfortable in her presence, trying to say consoling things to her. Sergeant Noonan wandered into the kitchen, came out quickly and said, "Look, Mrs. Maloney. You know that oven of yours is still on, and the meat still inside."

"Oh *dear* me!" she cried. "So it is!"

"I'd better turn it off for you, hadn't I?"

"Will you do that, Jack? Thank you so much."

When the sergeant returned the second time, she looked at him with her large, dark, tearful eyes. "Jack Noonan," she said.

"Yes?"

"Would you do me a small favour—you and these others?"

"We can try, Mrs. Maloney."

"Well," she said. "Here you all are, and good friends of dear Patrick's too, and helping to catch the man who killed him. You must be terribly hungry by now because it's long past your suppertime, and I know Patrick would never forgive me, God bless his soul, if I allowed you to remain in his house without offering you decent hospitality. Why don't you eat up the lamb that's in the oven? It'll be cooked just right by now."

"Wouldn't dream of it," Sergeant Noonan said.

"Please," she begged. "Please eat it. Personally, I couldn't touch a thing, certainly not what's been in the house when he was here. But it's all right for you. It'd be a favour to me if you'd eat it up. Then you can go on with your work again afterwards."

There was a good deal of hesitating among the four policemen, but they were clearly hungry, and in the end they were persuaded to go into the kitchen and help themselves. The woman stayed where she was, listening to them through the open door, and she could hear them speaking among themselves, their voices thick and sloppy because their mouths were full of meat.

"Have some more, Charlie?"

"No. Better not finish it."

"She *wants* us to finish it. She said so. Be doing her a favour."

"Okay then. Give me some more."

"That's a hell of a big club the guy must've used to hit poor Patrick," one of them was saying. "The doc says his skull was smashed all to pieces just like from a sledgehammer."

"That's why it ought to be easy to find."

"Exactly what I say."

"Whoever done it, they're not going to be

carrying a thing like that around with them longer than they need to."

One of them belched.

"Personally, I think it's right here on the premises."

"Probably right under our very noses. What'd you think, Jack?"

And in the other room, Mary Maloney began to giggle.

▲▼▶▼▶▲▼▶▼▶▲▼▶▼▶▲▼▶▼▶▲▶▶

TWINS

by Eric Wright

They looked very much alike, Lucy and her husband the mystery writer. This fact gave him an idea for the perfect crime.

I want to get it right," he said. "After making the mistake in the last book about how long it takes to get from Toronto to Detroit, I want this one to be water-tight. So just go along with me until I'm sure that it'll work."

They were standing on the edge of an old mine shaft about sixteen kilometres north of Sudbury. The shaft had been sunk in the thirties and they had had to claw their way through dense scrub pine to reach it, and pick the locks on two chain link fences that guarded the hole. At least it was too late in the year for mosquitoes. She wondered how he had found this place.

He seemed to hear what was in her mind. "I found it two years ago," he said. "I came up here hunting with Art. Someone told us we might find a bear along at the garbage dump but we missed the road and came to this place."

He was a writer of detective stories. As far as he could, he liked to "walk the course" of his plots until he was sure they would work. She always went along as a primary test that the story was possible. The stories often took them to some pleasant places, so it was like getting a second holiday, but this time she had come because she needed to know what was in his mind. Sudbury in October is not a popular vacation spot. "Tell me again," she said. "How does he get her to come this far? I wouldn't."

"You just did," he pointed out.

"That was research. Unless you make your villain a writer, you're going to have trouble. What is he, by the way?"

"I haven't decided yet. It's not important. I want to make sure this works, then I can flesh it out."

"Yes, but it doesn't work if the reader can't believe she would stumble through a half kilometre of bush in this godforsaken landscape. You've got to find a good reason."

"I'll find one. Let's get the plot straight, shall we?"

"This isn't the way you usually work. Usually you get the characters first, then let the plot grow out of them. So you say, anyway."

"Yeah, but this plot is ingenious. I mean, the villain thinks it is, so I want to test it before I spend my time creating his world. Okay?"

"Okay, so now he kills her. Right? And drops the body down there." She kicked a small rock over the edge of the hole and listened hard, but there was no "ploomp" or rattle of the sound of the rock reaching bottom. It must go down hundreds of metres.

"That's right. He throws the gun in after her; he's made sure it's untraceable. Then he drives south to the motel in Parry Sound where they have a reservation. When he gets there it's dark." He looked at the sky turning pink in the west. "He registers as her."

"Where did you get this idea?"

"From us. People are always saying we look alike, as if we're a couple of gerbils."

"Where does he change his clothes?"

"In the car, on a side road, probably the Pickerel River road, somewhere quiet. He doesn't actually have to change much: just put on a blonde wig, lipstick, glasses." He looked down at himself to show what he meant. Both of them were dressed in sneakers, blue jeans, and heavy bush jackets that came well below the waist. "Then he checks in at the motel, as her, saying 'her' husband is turning the car around or picking up beer or something. The point is the motel people have seen 'her' and believe that he is there, too. An hour later, he goes to the motel office, as himself, to ask for a wakeup call, so now the motel people have seen 'her' and him. Then, around midnight, the fighting starts. The people in the units on either side hear a hell of a row going on, sounds of someone being smacked around, and it goes on so long they complain to the desk, and the night clerk phones over and asks them to pipe down."

"The row is on tape, right?"

"Right. Then early in the morning the row starts again and there's a lot of door-banging and the neighbours see 'her' leaving, walking away. At breakfast time, he checks out leaving a message in case his wife returns. He tells the clerk she walked out on him during the night. She's probably gone to another motel. His message is that he's not going to wait around; he's gone home."

"So he left the motel in the blonde wig, then came back quietly as himself a bit later. Wasn't he taking a chance?"

"Not really. If anyone saw him, he could always say he had tried to follow his wife, but she disappeared. And that's that. He goes home and when his wife doesn't appear that day he reports it to the police. But in circumstances like these it looks likely that the wife has simply gone off somewhere. It's a few weeks before he can get the police seriously interested."

"And when they do take it seriously, do they find her?" There was not much light left now. In the east the sky was almost black.

"I don't know. It doesn't matter. A few weeks is as good as six months."

"They'll suspect him. After the row."

"But they won't be able to prove anything.

When he leaves the motel after breakfast, he checks in with the Ontario Provincial Police in Parry Sound, in case 'she' has checked in with them, and he does the same thing all the way down to Toronto, establishing a solid time trail with no gaps for him to drive back up to Sudbury. Then it's easy to make sure he's covered for the next week in Toronto."

"It might work," she said. "Have you figured out how you are going to solve it? How Porter will, I mean." Gib Porter was the writer's hero.

"Not yet."

"You could start with a hunch. You could find out what time he left Sudbury and why it took him five hours to get to Parry Sound. Did anyone see his car parked along the highway, stuff like that?"

"Why would anyone be suspicious?"

She pondered. "Her father. He never liked the man she married, never trusted him, so he hires Gib Porter." Now it was close to dark. "What about the car? Someone might have seen their car parked along the highway."

"It's rented. Perfectly ordinary rented car. If anyone sees it they won't memorize the licence plate. They'll just assume that it's a couple of hunters. But I haven't seen anyone around, have you?"

"No, I haven't. Who would be wandering around this moonscape?" She had to admit that he seemed to have everything covered. "One last thing," she asked. "Why? What's the reason?"

"Motive, you mean?" He shrugged. "Another woman, I guess."

"Come on. This is 1990. That was a motive back when you had to wait seven years for a divorce. People change around all the time now."

"Not if she refuses. The other lady, I mean. This guy has fallen in love with someone who refuses to see him until he is free. She was raised in the Brethren. She loves him, but she believes in the sanctity of marriage."

"Does she, indeed. It isn't his wife's fault, then." She turned her back on him and walked towards the road. She needed to know one more thing. "In the meantime, old buddy-boy," she said over her shoulder, "we'd better be getting back."

He reached inside his jacket and pulled out the little handgun he had bought in Detroit. "Don't turn round, Lucy," he said. She turned and saw that her last question was answered. It wasn't a game. She said, "It isn't going to work."

"It'll work, all right. It's going to work." He pulled the trigger once, twice, three times.

Everything else went smoothly. His wife had often criticized his plots for being too complicated, but this one worked. Two hours later the night clerk at the Sturgeon Motel in Parry Sound signed in Mrs. Harry Coates, a blonde lady with sun-glasses (though it was quite dark), while her husband unloaded the car. During the night, the clerk had to call them twice to ask them to pipe down because they were fighting and arguing so loudly that the guests on either side had called to complain. The rowing ended in the early morning with a lot of door-crashing, then Mrs. Coates came to the desk to check out. She still had sun-glasses on, but now the clerk thought they were probably covering up a black eye. Her husband, she said, had left her, taken a train or bus back to Toronto, maybe even hitch-hiked—she didn't know or care. She left a message for him in case he called. He never did, though.

She drove home and waited for two days for him to return, then she called the police. They made some routine enquiries, but they weren't very interested. The story of the night in the motel was clear, and the guy was almost certainly putting a scare into her by taking off for as long as his money held out, but pretty soon he would use a charge card or something like that, then they would be able to reel him in. They did establish that he had a girlfriend tucked away in a condominium on Sherbourne Street, and they kept an eye on her place but she was as mystified as they were, and he certainly never showed up. Nor did he try to call her. A month later the police assumed foul play and sent out a serious enquiry, and she began the process of establishing her legal position if he should have disappeared for good. When the first snow fell, she knew they wouldn't find him until the spring at the earliest, and then what would they find? A body, with no money in the wallet, and the gun that had killed him. (She had thrown *his* gun, from which she had removed the ammunition the night before they started their trip, when she realized what he was planning, into the French River on her way to Parry Sound.) And what would they conclude? That he had been picked up hitch-hiking, robbed and killed and dumped into the mineshaft by a local thug. There was still the very slight risk that someone had seen them when they went into the bush that evening, but it was a chance he was prepared to take, so it was pretty small. Since the chance of finding the body in the first place was about ten thousand to one, the further remote chance that someone saw them near the mineshaft was an acceptable risk. All she had to do was nurse her grief for the few weeks while the police made their enquiries.

The plan had been perfect, or pretty good. If she had not long known about the lady in the condominium, and if she had not come across his fishing tackle box with the loaded gun, the wig, and the make-up kit, packed ready to go, while she was searching for a pair of pliers, she would never have wondered what he was up to. After that it was just a matter of getting hold of a gun herself, and giving him every chance to prove her guess was wrong. The rest went exactly as he had planned.

3

Detectives To the Rescue

▲▼▶▼▲▼▶▼▶▼▲▼▶▼▶▼▲▼▶▼▼▶

ORIGIN OF THE DETECTIVE BUSINESS

by Newton Newkirk

Who was the first detective? Sherlock Holmes? Miss Marple? You may be surprised—the detective business is older than you think.

Adam was the first detective who ever happened. One day he woke up with a pain in his side.

"Gee-whizz," he exclaimed, "somebody has swiped one of my ribs." *(the first theft)*

"Here it is," said a sweet voice behind him. *(the first clue)*

Adam turned swiftly and beheld a beautiful woman. *(the first woman in the case)*

"Yuh-yuh-yes," gasped Adam, "there it is, but whatizzit?" *(the first mystery)*

"Why, I am your missing rib," replied the woman. *(the first confession)*

"Absurd," retorted Adam. "What is your name?" *(the first instance of cross-examination)*

"I am Eve," said the woman.

"Huh," snorted Adam, "you look more like 'September Morn.' " *(the first case of mistaken identity)*

Thereupon Eve blushed and excused herself. A few minutes later she returned wearing a modern fig-leaf costume—the waist had a plunging neckline and the skirt was slashed. *(the first disguise)*

Later Eve handed Adam what she called an apple. *(the first trap)*

After Adam bit into it he found it to be a *LEMON*. *(the first double cross)*

Right there is where the Serpent concealed in the tree overhead broke forth in a suppressed chuckle of mirth. *(the first detectaphone)*

One evening Adam came home from his daily toil, hungry and tired. He had been plowing on a steep hillside all day behind a refractory dinosaur and was hungrier than a couple of goats.

"I have a surprise for you, Adam," gushed Eve, as she kissed him on the front piazza. "Guess what?"

"Corned megatherium beef and cabbage," exclaimed Adam. *(the first theory)*

"Oh, pshaw, Adam, it isn't anything to eat—it is something the stork left on the front doorstep."

"Ah-ha," hissed Adam. "A girl?"

"No, not a girl," Eve replied; "guess again."

"Aw, shucks," sighed Adam; "I never was any good at guessing."

"Adam, you are the most stupid man I ever saw. Now, think hard—if it isn't a girl, what *must* it be?"

Adam pondered deeply a moment and then in a flash of almost human intelligence he exclaimed, "Ah, I know now—a BOY!" *(the first deduction by elimination)*

After supper Adam loaded his old shotgun and took his place on the doorstep. *(the first gunman)*

"What are you waiting for?" asked Eve.

"I'm waiting for that stork to come back," snapped Adam. *(the first threat)*

And so it was in the beginning ...

THE BIG HOLDUP

by Martin Gardner

Have fun trying to solve this picture puzzle (answer follows). You'll discover why detectives sometimes need to think like scientists in order to solve crimes.

Puzzle

When the discotheque's waiter reported for work, he heard shouting coming from the attic.

He rushed to the attic and found the manager with a rope around his waist and hanging from an overhead beam.

Manager: Quick. Get me down. Call the police. We've been robbed.

 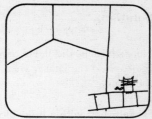

The manager told his story to the police.

Manager: Last night, after we closed, two robbers came and took all the money. Then they carried me to the attic and tied me to the beam.

The police believed his story because the attic room was completely empty. He couldn't have tied himself to the high beam, there was nothing to stand on. There was a stepladder used by the thieves, but it was just outside the door.

However, a few weeks later, the manager was arrested for robbing himself. Can you figure out how the manager, without any help, tied himself in mid-air?

Solution

Here's how he did it. He used the ladder to tie one end of the rope to the beam. Then he carried the ladder out of the room.

He returned with a huge block of ice he had prepared in the freezer.

He stood on the ice, tied the rope around himself and waited.

When the waiter found him the next day, all the ice had melted and the manager was left hanging in mid-air. Clever, wasn't he?

▲ ▶ ▼ ▶ ▲ ▼ ▶ ▼ ▶ ▲ ▼ ▶ ▼ ▶ ▲ ▼ ▶ ▼ ▲ ▶

THE PUNCHBOARDS

by Henry T. Parry

A punchboard is a kind of lottery. You choose a number on the board and punch out a slip of paper that tells you if you've won. But in this story, the slip of paper behind number 13 contains a clue—a clue that helps a 13-year-old boy to solve a murder.

I was writing a novel that summer about how this kid who was my age, thirteen, went out West to punch cattle for his uncle. It was all about the battles he and his uncle and his uncle's cowboys fought with this band of rustlers. Finally there is a big shootout and my hero finds himself in the middle of the street facing a rustler named Bad Sam Sears who is the fastest draw in the West. Bad Sam is standing there, holding his hands just above his two big guns, and sneering at my hero who's standing there, too, all alone, with nothing to hold his hands over.

I was walking back from my paper route one morning, trying to figure out how to get him out of this, when I saw a Ford roadster go tearing up North Main with Tommy Foulkes, our chief of police, and Johnny Herring, another policeman, in it. I ran up the street after them, figuring something big must have happened to get both of them out together.

They turned off on the road that led to the ball field. When I got there I saw that the chief had left the car just behind home plate—our ball field didn't have any fences and in the spring the outfield was sometimes used to pasture cows. He was busy underneath the bleachers, which I should explain was just a fancy name for four long homemade benches set back one above the other and shaded by a strip of canvas.

The chief, Johnny Herring, and Doc Stoneman were bent over the body of a girl. Standing behind me and looking even more green than usual was Two-Dip Dorsey, who ran the Kandy Kitchen in town. Two-Dip was a pretty big fellow, but now he looked scared.

"I was taking a shortcut over to North Main on my way to open the store," Two-Dip said to me, "when I seen something white laying there. When I go closer I see it's her. So I ran back home and called Doc Stoneman and Tommy Foulkes. But it ain't no use. She's dead."

"Who?"

"Helen Handey. One of that Handey tribe lives out on the Ridge Road."

There was this big family of Handeys, the

kind of people where if you walked by their place on Sunday morning you'd see Mrs. Handey and the girls all dressed up and leaving to walk to church and Old Man Handey and the boys in bib overalls with their heads stuck under the hood of a car. Somehow it worked out that the girls were all good people and the boys were kind of shiftless and plain no good. So that if it had been one of the Handey boys who had been found under the bleachers with his head busted in, everybody would have said, "I told you he wasn't coming to no good end."

"It was in the cards one of them Handey kids was going to have something like this happen," I heard Doc Stoneman say. "Looks like to me the girls ain't much better than the boys."

And what he was saying was what everybody else in town was saying, or anyway thinking, after a few days—like as if when someone is murdered it's somehow their fault. I heard them saying at Charley McCall's new store—Charley's the man I delivered papers for—that Helen Handey had put up a fight, judging from the way she was all scratched and bruised and the ground was all torn up. But I never heard that anybody agrees to be murdered, so how can it be their fault?

Doc Stoneman wasn't a doctor; he was the druggist, but he hadn't filled a prescription in years, not since Miss Hattie Snyder finished pharmacy school and came to work for him. Mostly Doc—who was a big, round man, kind of reddened and fleshy—would sit on a wire ice-cream-parlour chair under the two-bladed ceiling fan with his Panama hat on, figuring out the stock market. He took the *Journal of Commerce* that he always had to come into Charley's for because that paper didn't come in until the eight o'clock trolley from Weston while my papers came in on the six o'clock.

Doc was a spiffy dresser. He was the first in our town to have shoes of two colours and the first to wear those light striped summer suits—I think they're called seersucker—when nobody else in town would wear them because they looked like you were out on the street in your pyjamas. In his lapel Doc always wore a tiny pin, less than a centimetre. It was the kind of pin where the front part screws onto a back part through a buttonhole. It had three funny-looking letters on it. Eddie Heener, who jerks soda at Doc's, said it was a pledge pin for some fraternity at State that Doc had been asked to join when he went there for one term about a hundred years ago. "That ain't the real pin," Eddie explained, "but Doc's awful proud of it. It's just a sign you been asked to join. Doc puts it on whatever coat he's wearing. Them letters on it is Greek, Doc told me. When I asked Doc what they meant, he got mad and told me to get back to work. Doc only gets mad at me about five or six times a day."

Doc was a big eater, too. Often when I happened to be in his pharmacy I heard him say, "Four o'clock, Eddie," and Eddie would peel a banana, split it lengthwise, and lay it on one of those long silver sundae dishes. On top of that he'd put three dips of ice cream—chocolate, vanilla, and tutti-frutti. He'd give that a few squirts of chocolate syrup, spread on some crushed pineapple, and put a layer of marshmallow over the whole pile. I like sundaes an awful lot, but I don't think I could have eaten that even if I could have afforded it. Doc didn't have any trouble though. He'd tuck a paper napkin under his chin and start dipping away real slow, like he was trying to make it last. He was careful not to get any spots on his seersucker suit.

"Ain't a nicer man in town than Doc," Charley used to say, "so long as you don't ask him to do anything for anybody." But Charley was always saying things like that.

Besides playing the market, Doc did another thing I guess you could call gambling. That was taking a chance on one of Charley McCall's punchboards.

Every Friday morning about eight-thirty Doc would come into Charley's, put a dime down on the counter, and punch out number thirteen. Never any other number. If somebody had punched out number thirteen already, Doc would just wait until the next Friday. There weren't any numbers printed over the holes. Doc just punched out the first number in the second row, which was thirteen, because there were twelve numbers in a row.

A punchboard is made of hard, pressed paper a centimetre thick and measuring about twenty by thirty centimetres. It has about sixteen or twenty rows of holes, the holes plugged with rolled-up slips of paper, each slip with a number on it. You take something like a pencil or a skinny knitting needle, punch out a hole—the holes are covered front and back with paper pasted over them—and pull the rolled-up slip out from the back of the board. If the number on the slip matches a number printed on the top of the board, you win a prize. Most people didn't take the prizes they won, stuff that ran mostly to celluloid-backed brushes or Statues of Liberty made of metal so soft you expected it to melt. There were some better prizes, too, but most everybody sold them back to Charley to get the money. "Legitimate sales of merchandise," Charley called it.

For Doc, punching number thirteen every Friday morning was like somebody else being careful not to step on the cracks on the sidewalk. I heard Charley telling someone about it, and he used a fancy word. "Obsessive," Charley said. I knew it must have been a word that Charley had just heard of, because he used it about six times in the next ten minutes.

Doc Stoneman may have thought it was Helen Handey's fault that she got murdered, but Tommy Foulkes didn't think so. He got the county detectives in and later the state police. But nobody ever found out anything except that Helen had left the house around seven-thirty in the evening and hadn't come back.

The Handeys said she'd been doing this about once a week since Christmas, but she'd never say where she was going or if she was meeting anyone. Sometimes she said she was going down the road to meet her friend Tilly Smith, but she was all dressed up so it wasn't likely she was spending much time with Tilly.

The thing that's hard to explain is how anybody in our town could be doing something for eight months without everybody knowing it. It was pretty hard to change your mind without somebody asking how come. Anyway, a couple of weeks went by and nobody found out who had murdered poor Helen Handey—and it looked like nobody ever would.

I was still fussing with my novel—couldn't figure out a way to keep Bad Sam Sears from killing the hero in the showdown—when I got the idea that maybe I should write a detective story instead. I thought I could make the story sound more real if I visited the scene of a crime. Well, the only crime we ever had in our town was the murder of Helen Handey, so I went out to the ball field and looked around under the bleachers where Two-Dip Dorsey had found the body. It made me feel scared to think about what had happened here just a few weeks ago, right where I was standing, right in the same air space I was taking up, where someone had fought hard to stay alive and had lost.

I'd heard Charley McCall say the police had gone over the ground with a rake and hadn't found anything. Now the ground was littered over with the same stuff you always see around a ball field—wrappers from candy bars, empty cigarette packs, Crackerjack boxes, bottle caps, and empty soft-drink bottles. The grass was flattened from trampling, but there was some Queen Anne's lace and some skunk cabbage standing around the foot of one of the uprights. I figured the best way to search the place was to take away everything that was there because of people eating, drinking, and smoking while watching the game. So I picked up every bit of trash I could find and made a pile of it behind the bleachers. Then I looked carefully, down on my hands and knees, at every speck of ground.

I didn't find anything except the cap of a Moxie bottle pressed down into the ground. I pried it up and flicked it onto the trash pile. Then I saw stuck to it, under it, the pin with the Greek letters I'd seen a hundred times on Doc Stoneman's lapel. I pulled it loose and held it in my hand, just staring at it, scared of it because of what it stood for. What I had started doing just to help me in writing a story had ended up connecting me with a happening out of real life—a dark, frightening, murderous happening, nothing at all like the story that I had in my head.

I suppose I should have looked for more clues, but I had to stop because a bunch of kids were coming across the outfield and would have made a lot of smart remarks about what I was doing crawling around under the bleachers. But mostly I wanted to get rid of that pin.

When I went into police headquarters, which was a fancy name for one room on the first floor rear of the town hall, I found Chief Foulkes and Johnny Herring bent over the checkerboard. At least Johnny was bent. The chief was reading the newspaper, waiting for Johnny to move. Tommy was a big, white-haired man with blue eyes that looked like he was thinking of something else while you were talking to him. There were people in town who said that Tommy talked slow and moved slow and the only thing he did fast was think. I told them how I came to be rooting around under the bleachers, and I held out my hand with the pledge pin in it.

"Hey, that's Doc Stoneman's," Johnny said. "He's been wearing that little doohickey ever since I knew him."

Tommy proceeded to ask me a lot of questions, but I couldn't tell him much more than I already had.

"Shows Tilly Smith was telling us the truth," Johnny said. "She said she hadn't seen Helen except in church since around Christmas, when Helen said she might be getting married soon and she shouldn't tell anybody. So when Helen was going out and nobody knew where she was going, she was meeting Doc out at the ball field. They got into some kind of fracas, maybe about getting married, and Doc kills her. You know how quick he flies off the handle. Stands to reason, don't it?"

"Doc could have lost that pin while he was watching a ballgame."

"Tommy, you know as well as I do that Doc ain't never been to a game since he played for the high school. He ain't been more than five blocks from his store in twenty years."

Tommy gave a deep sigh and kept quiet. He kind of squeezed his mouth with his left hand and looked at me a long time. I kept hoping Johnny Herring would keep on talking, but he didn't.

"We want that you should keep quiet about what you found," Tommy said to me after a bit. "That would help us a lot."

Folks said that when Tommy Foulkes talked to you, it didn't make any difference if you were a kid or if you were old—say, thirty—you got the feeling he expected you to agree with him, as if there had always been some understanding between him and you about how things were. Well, that's the way I felt, and for the next couple of days I went around with this secret busting inside me. I could imagine Tommy Foulkes having meetings with the county detectives and the state police, discussing what they should do with what I'd found and probably mentioning my name any number of times. And at least two guys on my street said they could hardly stand being around anybody as important as I seemed to think I was.

A couple of mornings later—a Friday—I'd come in
from my paper route and was hanging around
Charley's, sneaking a free read from the magazines,
when Charley asked me to watch the store, which
he usually did about twice a week. This time
Charley said he wanted to meet the trolley and
have it out with Skooks Decker, the motorman,
who Charley said was helping himself to a paper
out of the bundle he brought up from Weston. I
guess maybe Skooks was, because folks said
Skooks had a habit of reading a newspaper while
he was running the trolley.

This morning Doc Stoneman came in,
plunked a dime down on the counter, and pointed
at the punchboard. I rang up his dime and watched
him punch out the thirteenth hole. He read the slip,
tossed it on the floor, and walked out the door, not
saying anything. I noticed he wasn't wearing that
pin in his lapel. But if Tommy Foulkes or any of the
other police had talked to him about Helen
Handey, it didn't seem to have bothered Doc none.
To me, he seemed the same as he always had.
Noticing the slip of punchboard paper he'd tossed
on the floor, this great idea came to me about how I
could find out if Doc really had anything to do
with Helen Handey.

I hung around Charley's as much as I could so I
could pick up the slips of paper people punched

out of the punchboards and tossed away. Charley asked me if I was sick or something, because he never once had seen me pick up one single, solitary, earthly thing from the floor before. I spent hours practising printing real small on the slips I picked up.

When I had it down pretty good, I wrote out three messages on three slips. Charley generally had three punchboards in stock, so one day when I was alone in the store—Charley had gone over to the town hall to argue with Lon Adams about his tax assessment—I took a pin and carefully picked holes in the back of the punchboard around the edges of the thirteenth hole, leaving a little lid held by a hinge of uncut paper. I pushed the open ends of a hairpin into the hole, squeezed the ends together, pulled out the slips of paper, and replaced them with the slips I had written on. Then I stuck the lids back down. It's funny, people would notice right away if you tampered with the front of the board, but it never occurs to anyone to turn the board over to see if the back has been messed with. And once you've punched out a hole, you naturally expect the paper covering that hole in the back of the board to be broken open. I put the boards back in the drawer in the order I wanted Charley to take them out.

The next Friday morning when Doc came in and put down his dime, I watched him pretty close. Charley handed him the first board I doctored. Doc punched out the paper, unrolled it, and read it. He jerked his head up to see if anyone was watching, but Charley was reading the cash register and Doc hardly knew I was there. He gave his glasses a poke and went to the door to read the slip in a better light, then put the slip in his pocket instead of tossing it on the floor. When Charley said, "No luck, hunh, Doc?" Doc didn't answer; he just walked out. What I'd written on the slip was *Hi, Doc. Helen.*

The second Friday was about the same, except Charley had stepped out. I handed Doc the second board, and he punched out the thirteenth hole. He unrolled the paper and smoothed it over and over as if he couldn't bring himself to read it. Finally he did, and his face went grey and broke out in sweat. He walked out of the store, his big stomach banging against the screen door because he hadn't pushed it open ahead of him. This message read *How about it, Doc? Helen.*

I saw Doc twice the next week, meeting him as he was coming into town on North Main Street as I was headed out with my papers. I asked him what he was doing up so early, and he mumbled something about taking a walk because he couldn't sleep. He looked like he'd been sick and that seersucker suit on him looked like it should have been worn by a much larger man, even though Doc was pretty big.

On the third Friday Doc read the slip I'd planted and groped his way out of the store. "What's got into Doc?" Charley asked. "Seems like he's sleepwalking or something." What had got into Doc was the third message: *Tonight, Doc. Same place. Helen.*

That night as soon as it got dark I said something about going downtown for a soda. I went up North Main to the ball field and sat down on the top row of bleachers, right over the place where Two-Dip Dorsey had found the body of Helen Handey. It was a beautiful night, deep summer, with a full moon, an owl beginning to stir over in Harris's Woods, and the sound of water flowing over the wall of Keller's Dam.

The road off North Main Street ends right where centre field begins. I saw a car without lights stop out there where people usually park when there's a game. In the moonlight I could see a man, a big man, coming slowly in from centre field, across second base, and over the pitcher's mound to home plate, where he turned around and looked at the diamond as though he was seeing again the old games that had been played there back in the days when everybody was young and the town had been a friendly, easygoing place, maybe before something was done that now couldn't be undone. I don't know. Anyway, the man turned, came around the backstop, and went around and under the bleachers. A big fear wrenched at my stomach when the thought struck me that maybe he had a flashlight. I could hear him below me, not one metre away.

"Helen."

He said it as though he wanted to talk and at the same time didn't want to talk and so had settled on a whisper. I felt myself go cold and queer, because something had come into my mind from someplace deep in it that I didn't know was there, something that made me expect to hear someone answer him, someone I'd seen lying dead on the ground below where I was sitting.

"Helen! Forgive! Please! Forgive!"

I heard him make a long moaning noise as he turned away. He went back the way he came— home plate, pitcher's mound, second base, and centre field. The car door slammed.

I took off straight for the town hall to tell Tommy Foulkes what I'd seen, but police headquarters were dark and locked up. The next morning first thing I went back to headquarters and there wasn't anyone there.

I was heading to Charley's to pick up my papers when I saw Charley and about a dozen others from up the block staring into the windows of Doc's pharmacy. It was pretty early for that many people to be hanging around, so I went to see what was going on.

I looked in the window, and there was Doc seated in his wire chair under the two-bladed fan, dressed in his seersucker suit and wearing his Panama hat. Standing behind him was Doc Simmons, who was a medical doctor, and Tommy Foulkes. Miss Hattie Snyder, the pharmacist, was in there, too, dabbing at her eyes with a paper napkin.

"Seems Hattie came in early to fix a prescription for old Miss Berger out on Second Street," Charley was saying. "She found Doc sitting there at the table with a napkin under his chin. He'd put together one of those big sundaes he had every day and had polished it off. Then, from what Hattie says, he must have fixed himself something from the pharmacy. They ain't sure yet. The coroner will have to find out."

▲ ▼ ▶ ▶ ▲ ▼ ▶ ▼ ▶ ▲ ▼ ▶ ▼ ▶ ▲ ▼ ▶ ▼ ▶ ▶

FINGERPRINTS TELL TALES

by Martha G. Webb

Martha Webb is a mystery writer with real-life experience in detective work. She claims that fingerprints still give the best evidence at the scene of the crime.

I've worked real crimes, and I've written fictional ones.

Fictional ones are neater.

They don't start at two a.m. unless you want them to. You don't have to collect unmentionable goop off the wall and ceiling and make diagrams of where you got it from, and nobody's having hysterics in the next room.

But the biggest difference is all those little coincidences and loose ends. In fiction they all have to fit. You make a list and tack it to your wall: loose ends I have to tie up in the last chapter. In real life the loose ends stick out everywhere, and most of the time you never do find out where the killer hid the victim's car keys and why, or what the winos were fighting about the week before one of them turned up dead in a bamboo thicket. Often the loose ends are tied up, and the coincidences worked out, only by physical evidence.

The best physical evidence, bar none, is fingerprints.

I was a latent fingerprint examiner before I started writing mysteries. Fingerprints aren't used in fiction as much as they used to be; would-be sophisticates tend to say things like "Criminals now are too smart to leave prints." That's not so. The prints are there, and they work just as well as they ever did. You can do amazing things with them, things I'd never dare write in a novel.

I still laugh whenever I think about one case. The victim—that is, the primary victim—was an auto repair shop. Sometime during the night several juveniles broke in, and by morning the chaos couldn't be described in words; I had to diagram it. The kids had driven, and wrecked, twelve different vehicles that had been left for repair, besides creating sundry other havoc.

It was hot that night, and the kids were sweating; furthermore, all three of them were barefoot. While Lt. Ronnie King was tracking their footprints quite easily down the alley to their homes, I was sorting out who did what where and in what order. This was easy enough to do, because the position the cars had halted in, and the way footprints were piled on footprints, told me the precise sequence.

That afternoon, after all the other work on the

case had been done, Ronnie tiredly marched one of the twelve-year-old culprits across the hall to me and said, "He still denies it. How about you have a talk with him?"

I laid my diagram out on the table. "Now, let me tell you what you did," I said. "You drove this car and wrecked it. You couldn't get this one started, so you went through the glove box looking for money." Horrified comprehension was dawning on the kid's face as I continued: "Then you went in the office and tasted the candy and decided you didn't like it and spat it out. Then you took the Polaroid, carried it to the jeep, and—"

His voice shaking, the kid asked, "Lady, where was you hidin'?"

▲▼▶▼▲▼▶▼▲▼▶▼▲▼▶▼▲▼▶▼▶▶

THE CASE OF THE DENTIST'S PATIENT

by Donald J. Sobol

Dr. Haledjian is a detective created by the author of the *Encyclopedia Brown* books. Now that you've picked up lots of clues about detective work, see if you can solve this next case as quickly as Dr. Haledjian does. (Answer is at the end of story.)

Dr. Evelyn Williams, London-born New York dentist, was preparing to take a wax impression of the right lower teeth of his patient, Dorothy Hoover. Silently the door behind him opened. A gloved hand holding an automatic appeared.

Two shots sounded, Miss Hoover slumped over, dead.

"We've got a suspect," Inspector Winters told Dr. Haledjian at his office an hour afterward. "The elevator boy took a nervous man to the fifteenth floor—Dr. Williams has one of six offices on the floor—a few moments before the shooting. The description fits John 'Torpedo' Burton.

"Burton is out on parole," continued the inspector. "I had him picked up at his rooming house. As far as he knows, I want to question him about a minor parole infraction."

Burton was ushered in and angrily demanded, "What's this all about?"

"Ever hear of Dr. Evelyn Williams?" asked the inspector.

"No, why?"

"Dorothy Hoover was shot to death less than two hours ago as she sat in a chair in Dr. Williams' office."

"I been sleeping all afternoon."

"An elevator operator says he took a man answering your description to the fifteenth floor a moment before the shots."

"It wasn't me," snarled Burton. "I look like a lot of guys. I ain't been near a dentist's office since Sing Sing. This Williams, I bet he never saw me, so what can you prove?"

"Enough," snapped Dr. Haledjian, "to send you to the chair!"

What was the basis of Haledjian's remark?

Answer

Although Burton claimed never to have heard of a Dr. Evelyn Williams, he knew the doctor was (1) a dentist, and (2) a man.

▲▶▼▲▶▼▶▼▲▶▼▶▼▲▶▼▶▼

PUZZLE FOR POPPY

by Patrick Quentin

Who would want to harm a lovable Saint Bernard? Someone who knows that Poppy is one of the richest dogs in the world! Miss Crump turns to her new neighbour—movie star Iris Duluth—for help.

Yes, Miss Crump," snapped Iris into the phone. "No, Miss Crump. Oh, nuts, Miss Crump."

My wife flung down the receiver.

"Well?" I asked.

"She won't let us use the patio. It's that dog, that great fat Saint Bernard. It mustn't be disturbed."

"Why?"

"It has to be alone with its beautiful thoughts. It's going to become a mother. Peter, it's revolting. There must be something in the lease."

"There isn't," I said.

When I rented our half of the La Jolla hacienda for my shore leave, the lease specified that all rights to the enclosed patio belonged to our eccentric co-tenant. It oughtn't to have mattered, but it did because Iris had recently skyrocketed to fame as a movie star and it was impossible for us to appear on the streets without being mobbed. For the last couple of days we had been virtually beleauguered in our apartment. We were crazy about being beleaguered together, but even Heloise and Abelard needed a little fresh air once in a while.

That's why the patio was so important.

Iris was staring through the locked French windows at the forbidden delights of the patio. Suddenly she turned.

"Peter, I'll die if I don't get things into my lungs—ozone and things. We'll just have to go to the beach."

"And be torn limb from limb by your public again?"

"I'm sorry, darling. I'm terrible sorry." Iris unzipped herself from her housecoat and scrambled into slacks and a shirt-waist. She tossed me my naval hat.

"Come, Lieutenant—to the slaughter."

When we emerged on the street, we collided head-on with a man carrying groceries into the house. As we disentangled ourselves from celery stalks, there was a click and a squeal of delight followed by a powerful whistle. I turned to see a small girl who had been lying in wait with a camera. She was an unsightly little girl with sandy pigtails and braces on her teeth.

"Gee," she announced. "I can get two buckth for thith thnap from Barney Thtone. He'th thappy about you, Mith Duluth."

Other children, materializing in response to her whistle, were galloping toward us. The grocery man came out of the house. Passers-by stopped, stared and closed in—a woman in scarlet slacks, two sailors, a flurry of bobby-soxers, a policeman.

"This," said Iris grimly, "is the end."

She escaped from her fans and marched back to the two front doors of our hacienda. She rang the buzzer on the door that wasn't ours. She rang persistently. At length there was the clatter of a chain sliding into place and the door opened wide enough to reveal the face of Miss Crump. It was a small, faded face with a most uncordial expression.

"Yes?" asked Miss Crump.

"We're the Duluths," said Iris. "I just called you. I know about your dog, but ..."

"Not *my* dog," corrected Miss Crump. "Mrs. Wilberframe's dog. The late Mrs. Wilberframe of Glendale who has a nephew and a niece-in-law of whom I know a great deal in Ogden Bluffs, Utah. At least, they *ought* to be in Ogden Bluffs."

This unnecessary information was flung at us like a challenge. Then Miss Crump's face flushed into sudden dimpled pleasure.

"Duluth! Iris Duluth. You're *the* Iris Duluth of the movies?"

"Yes," said Iris.

"Oh, why didn't you tell me over the phone?

My favourite actress! How exciting! Poor thing—mobbed by your fans. Of course you may use the patio. I will give you the key to open your French windows. Any time."

Miraculously the chain was off the door. It opened halfway and then stopped. Miss Crump was staring at me with a return of suspicion.

"You *are* Miss Duluth's husband?"

"Mrs. Duluth's husband," I corrected her. "Lieutenant Duluth."

She still peered. "I mean, you have proof?"

I was beyond being surprised by Miss Crump. I fumbled from my wallet a dog-eared snapshot of Iris and me in full wedding regalia outside the church. Miss Crump studied it carefully and then returned it.

"You must please excuse me. What a sweet bride! It's just that I can't be too careful—for Poppy."

"Poppy?" queried Iris. "The Saint Bernard?"

Miss Crump nodded. "It is Poppy's house, you see. Poppy pays the rent."

"The dog," said Iris faintly, "pays the rent?"

"Yes, my dear. Poppy is very well-to-do. She is hardly more than a puppy, but she is one of the richest dogs, I suppose, in the whole world."

Although we entertained grave doubts as to Miss Crump's sanity, we were soon in swimming suits and stepping through our open French windows into the sunshine of the patio. Miss Crump introduced us to Poppy.

In spite of our former prejudices, Poppy disarmed us immediately. She was just a big, bouncing, natural girl unspoiled by wealth. She greeted us with great thumps of her tail. She leaped up at Iris, dabbing at her cheek with a long, pink tongue. Later, when we had settled on striped mattresses under orange trees, she curled into a big clumsy ball at my side and laid her vast muzzle on my stomach.

"Look, she likes you." Miss Crump was glowing. "Oh, I knew she would!"

Iris, luxuriating in the sunshine, asked the polite question. "Tell us about Poppy. How did she make her money?"

"Oh, she did not make it. She inherited it." Miss Crump sat down on a white iron chair. "Mrs. Wilberframe was a very wealthy woman. She was devoted to Poppy."

"And left her all her money?" I asked.

"Not quite all. There was a little nest egg for me. I was her companion, you see, for many years. But I am to look after Poppy. That is why I received the nest egg. Poppy pays me a generous salary too." She fingered nondescript beads at her throat. "Mrs. Wilberframe was anxious for Poppy to have only the best and I am sure I try to do the right thing. Poppy has the master bedroom, of course. I take the little one in front. And then if Poppy has steak for dinner, I have hamburger." She stared intensely. "I would not have an easy moment if I felt that Poppy did not get the best."

Poppy, her head on my stomach, coughed. She banged her tail against the flagstones apologetically.

Iris reached across me to pat her. "Has she been rich for long?"

"Oh, no. Mrs Wilberframe passed on only a few weeks ago." Miss Crump paused. "And it has been a great responsibility for me." She paused again and then blurted: "You're my friends, aren't you? Oh, I am sure you are. Please, please, won't you help me? I am all alone and I am so frightened."

"Frightened?" I looked up and, sure enough, her little bird face was peaked with fear.

"For Poppy." Miss Crump leaned forward. "Oh, Lieutenant, it is like a nightmare. Because I know. I just know they are trying to murder her!"

"They?" Iris sat up straight.

"Mrs. Wilberframe's nephew and his wife. From Ogden Bluffs, Utah."

"You mentioned them when you opened the door."

"I mention them to everyone who comes to the house. You see, I do not want them to think I am not on my guard."

I watched her. She might have looked like a silly spinster with a bee in her bonnet. She didn't. She looked nice and quite sane, only scared.

"Oh, they are not good people. Not at all. There is nothing they would not stoop to. Back in Glendale, I found pieces of meat in the front yard.

Poisoned meat, I know. And on a lonely road, they shot at Poppy. Oh, the police laughed at me. A car backfiring, they said. But I know differently. I know they won't stop till Poppy is dead." She threw her little hands up to her face. "I ran away from them in Glendale. That is why I came to La Jolla. But they have caught up with us. I know. Oh dear, poor Poppy who is so sweet without a nasty thought in her head."

Poppy, hearing her name mentioned, smiled and panted.

"But this nephew and his wife from Ogden Bluffs, why should they want to murder her?" My wife's eyes were gleaming with a detective enthusiasm I knew of old. "Are they after her money?"

"Of course," said Miss Crump passionately. "It's the will. The nephew is Mrs. Wilberframe's only living relative, but she deliberately cut him off and I am sure I do not blame her. All the money goes to Poppy and—er—Poppy's little ones."

"Isn't the nephew contesting a screwy will like that?" I asked.

"Not yet. To contest a will takes a great deal of money—lawyer fees—and things. It would be much, much cheaper for him to kill Poppy. You see, one thing is not covered by the will. If Poppy were to die before she became a mother, the nephew would inherit the whole estate. Oh, I have done everything in my power. The moment the—er—suitable season arrived, I found a husband for

Poppy. In a few weeks now, the little ones are expected. But these next few weeks ..."

Miss Crump dabbed at her eyes with a small handkerchief. "Oh, the Glendale police were most unsympathetic. They even mentioned the fact that the sentence for shooting or killing a dog in this state is shockingly light—a small fine at most. I called the police here and asked for protection. They said they'd send a man around sometime but they were hardly civil. So you see, there is no protection from the law and no redress. There is no one to help me."

"You've got us," said Iris in a burst of sympathy.

"Oh ... oh ..." The handkerchief fluttered from Miss Crump's face. "I knew you were my friends. You dear, dear things. Oh, Poppy, they are going to help us."

Poppy, busy licking my stomach, did not reply. Somewhat appalled by Iris' hasty promise but ready to stand by her, I said:

"Sure, we'll help, Miss Crump. First, what's the nephew's name?"

"Henry. Henry Blodgett. But he won't use that name. Oh, no, he will be too clever for that."

"And you don't know what he looks like?"

"Mrs. Wilberframe destroyed his photograph many years ago when he bit her as a small boy. With yellow curls, I understand. That is when the trouble between them started."

"At least you know what age he is?"

"He should be about thirty."

"And the wife?" asked Iris.

"I know nothing about her," said Miss Crump coldly, "except that she is supposed to be a red-headed person, a former actress."

"And what makes you so sure one or both of them have come to La Jolla?"

Miss Crump folded her arms in her lap. "Last night. A telephone call."

"A telephone call?"

"A voice asking if I was Miss Crump, and then—silence." Miss Crump leaned toward me. "Oh, now they know I am here. They know I never let Poppy out. They know every morning I search the patio for meat, traps. They must realize that the only possible way to reach her is to enter the house."

"Break in?"

Miss Crump shook her tight curls. "It is possible. But I believe they will rely on guile rather than violence. It is against that we must be on our guard. You are the only people who have come to the door since that telephone call. Now anyone else that comes to your apartment or mine, whatever their excuse ..." She lowered her voice. "Anyone may be Henry Blodgett or his wife and we will have to outwit them."

A fly settled on one of Poppy's valuable ears. She did not seem to notice it. Miss Crump watched us earnestly and then gave a self-scolding cluck.

"Dear me, here I have been burdening you

with Poppy's problems and you must be hungry. How about a little salad for luncheon? I always feel guilty about eating in the middle of the day when Poppy has her one meal at night. But with guests—yes, and allies—I am sure Mrs. Wilberframe would not have grudged the expense."

With a smile that was half-shy, half conspiratorial, she fluttered away.

I looked at Iris, "Well," I said, "is she a nut or do we believe her?"

"I rather think," said my wife, "that we believe her."

"Why?"

"Just because." Iris' face wore the entranced expression which had won her so many fans in her last picture. "Oh, Peter, don't you see what fun it will be? A beautiful Saint Bernard in peril. A wicked villain with golden curls who bit his aunt."

"He won't have golden curls any more," I said. "He's a big boy now."

Iris, her body warm from the sun, leaned over me and put both arms around Poppy's massive neck.

"Poor Poppy," she said. "Really, this shouldn't happen to a dog!"

The first thing happened some hours after Miss Crump's little salad luncheon while Iris and I were sunning ourselves. Miss Crump, who had been preparing Poppy's dinner and her own in her apartment, came running to announce:

"There is a man at the door! He claims he is from the electric light company to read the meter. Oh, dear, if he is legitimate and we do not let him in, there will be trouble with the electric light company and if ..." She wrung her hands. "Oh, what shall we do?"

I reached for a bathrobe. "You and Iris stay here. And for Mrs. Wilberframe's sake, hang onto Poppy."

I found the man outside the locked front door. He was about thirty with thinning hair and wore an army discharge button. He showed me his credentials. They seemed in perfect order. There was nothing for it but to let him in. I took him into the kitchen where Poppy's luscious steak and Miss Crump's modest hamburger were lying where Miss Crump had left them on the table. I hovered over the man while he located the meter. I never let him out of my sight until he had departed. In answer to Miss Crump's anxious questioning, I could only say that if the man had been Henry Blodgett he knew how much electricity she'd used in the past month——but that was all.

The next caller showed up a few minutes later. Leaving Iris, indignant at being out of things, to stand by Poppy, Miss Crump and I handled the visitor. This time it was a slim, brash girl with bright auburn hair and a navy-blue slack suit. She was, she said, the sister of the woman who owned the hacienda. She wanted a photograph for the newspapers——a photograph of her Uncle William who had just been promoted to Rear Admiral in the Pacific. The photograph was in a trunk in the attic.

Miss Crump, reacting to the unlikeliness of the request, refused entry. The red-head wasn't the type that wilted. When she started talking darkly of eviction, I overrode Miss Crump and offered to conduct her to the attic. The girl gave me one quick experienced look and flounced into the hall.

The attic was reached by the back stairs through the kitchen. I conducted the red-head directly to her claimed destination. There were trunks. She searched through them. At length she produced a photograph of a limp young man in a raccoon coat.

"My Uncle William," she snapped, "as a youth."

"Pretty," I said.

I took her back to the front door and she left. If she had been Mrs. Blodgett, she knew how to take care of herself, she knew how many trunks there were in the attic—and that was all.

Iris and I dressed and were drinking Daiquiris under a green-and-white-striped umbrella when Miss Crump appeared followed by a young policeman. He had come, she said, in answer to her complaint. She showed him Poppy; she babbled out her story of the Blodgetts. He obviously thought she was a harmless lunatic, but she didn't seem to realize it. After she had let him out, she settled beamingly down with us.

"I suppose," said Iris, "you asked him for his

credentials?"

"I ..." Miss Crump's face clouded. "My dear, you don't think that perhaps he wasn't a real police ...?"

"To me," said Iris, "everyone's a Blodgett until proved to the contrary."

"Oh, dear," said Miss Crump.

Nothing else happened. By evening Iris and I were back in our part of the house. Poppy had hated to see us go. We had hated to leave her. A mutual crush had developed between us.

But now that we were alone again, the sinister Blodgetts did not seem very substantial. Iris made a creditable *Boeuf Stroganov* from yesterday's leftovers and changed into a lime-green negligee. I was busy pretending to be a sailor on leave when the phone rang. I reached over Iris for the receiver, said "Hello," and then sat rigid listening.

It was Miss Crump's voice. But something was horribly wrong with it. It came across hoarse and gasping.

"Come," it said. "Oh, come. The French windows. Oh, please ..."

The voice faded. I heard the clatter of a dropped receiver.

"It must be Poppy," I said to Iris. "Quick!"

We ran out into the dark patio. Across it, I could see the French windows of Miss Crump's apartment. They were half open, and as I looked Poppy squirmed through to the patio. She bounded toward us, whining.

"Poppy's all right," said Iris. "Quick!"

We ran to Miss Crump's windows. Poppy barged past us into the living room. We followed. All the lights were on. Poppy had galloped around a high-backed davenport. We went to it and looked over it.

Poppy was crouching on the carpet, her huge muzzle dropped on her paws. She was howling and staring straight at Miss Crump.

Poppy's paid companion was on the floor too. She lay motionless on her back, her legs twisted under her, her small, grey face distorted, her lips stretched in a dreadful smile.

I knelt down by Poppy. I picked up Miss Crump's thin wrist and felt for the pulse. Poppy was still howling. Iris stood, straight and white.

"Peter, tell me. Is she dead?"

"Not quite. But only just not quite. Poison. It looks like strychnine ..."

We called a doctor. We called the police. The doctor came, muttered a shocked diagnosis of strychnine poisoning and rushed Miss Crump to the hospital. I asked if she had a chance. He didn't answer. I knew what that meant. Soon the police came and there was so much to say and do and think that I hadn't time to brood about poor Miss Crump.

We told Inspector Green the Blodgett story. It was obvious to us that somehow Miss Crump had been poisoned by them in mistake for Poppy. Since no one had entered the house that day except three callers, one of them, we said, must have been a

Blodgett. All the Inspector had to do, we said, was to locate those three people and find out which was a Blodgett.

Inspector Green watched us pokerfaced and made no comment. After he'd left, we took the companionless Poppy back to our part of the house. She climbed on the bed and stretched out between us, her tail thumping, her head flopped on the pillows. We didn't have the heart to evict her. It was not one of our better nights.

Early next morning, a policeman took us to Miss Crump's apartment. Inspector Green was waiting in the living room. I didn't like his stare.

"We've analyzed the hamburger she was eating last night," he said. "There was enough strychnine in it to kill an elephant."

"Hamburger!" exclaimed Iris. "Then that proves she was poisoned by the Blodgetts!"

"Why?" asked Inspector Green.

"They didn't know how conscientious Miss Crump was. They didn't know she always bought steak for Poppy and hamburger for herself. They saw the steak and the hamburger and they naturally assumed the hamburger was for Poppy, so they poisoned that."

"That's right," I cut in. "The steak and the hamburger were lying right on the kitchen table when all three of those people came in yesterday."

"I see," said the Inspector.

He nodded to a policeman who left the room and returned with three people—the balding young man from the electric light company, the red-headed vixen, and the young policeman. None of them looked happy.

"You're willing to swear," the Inspector asked us, "that these were the only three people who entered this house yesterday."

"Yes," said Iris.

"And you think one of them is either Blodgett or his wife?"

"They've got to be."

Inspector Green smiled faintly. "Mr. Burns here has been with the electric light company for five years except for a year when he was in the army. The electric light company is willing to vouch for that. Miss Curtis has been identified as the sister of the lady who owns this house and the niece of Rear Admiral Moss. She has no connection with any Blodgetts and has never been in Utah." He paused. "As for Officer Patterson, he has been a member of the police force here for eight years. I personally sent him around yesterday to follow up Miss Crump's complaint."

The Inspector produced an envelope from his pocket and tossed it to me. "I've had these photographs of Mr. and Mrs. Henry Blodgett flown from the files of the Ogden Bluffs *Tribune*."

I pulled the photographs out of the envelope. We stared at them. Neither Mr. or Mrs. Blodgett looked at all the sort of person you would like to know. But neither of them bore the slightest resemblance to any of the three suspects in front of us.

"It might also interest you," said the Inspector quietly, "that I've checked with the Ogden Bluffs police. Mr. Blodgett has been sick in bed for over a week and his wife has been nursing him. There is a doctor's certificate to that effect."

Inspector Green gazed down at his hands. They were competent hands. "It looks to me that the whole Blodgett story was built up in Miss Crump's mind—or yours." His grey eyes stared right through us. "If we have to eliminate the Blodgetts and these three people from suspicion, that leaves only two others who had the slightest chance of poisoning the hamburger."

Iris blinked. "Us?"

"You," said Inspector Green almost sadly.

They didn't arrest us, of course. We had no conceivable motive. But Inspector Green questioned us minutely and when he left there was a policeman lounging outside the door.

We spent a harried afternoon racking our brains and getting nowhere. Iris was one who had the inspiration. Suddenly, just after she had fed Poppy the remains of the *Stroganov*, she exclaimed:

"Good heavens above, of course!"

"Of course what?"

She spun to me, her eyes shining. "Barney Thtone," she lisped. "Why didn't we realize? Come on!"

She ran out of the house into the street. She

grabbed the lounging policeman by the arm.

"You live here," she said. "Who's Barney Stone?"

"Barney Stone?" The policeman stared. "He's the son of the druggist on the corner."

Iris raced me to the drugstore. She was attracting quite a crowd. The policeman followed, too.

In the drugstore, a thin young man with spectacles stood behind the prescription counter.

"Mr. Stone?" asked Iris.

His mouth dropped open. "Gee, Miss Duluth. I never dreamed ... Gee, Miss Duluth, what can I do for you? Cigarettes? An alarm clock?"

"A little girl," said Iris. "A little girl with sandy pigtails and braces on her teeth. What's her name? Where does she live?"

Barney Stone said promptly: "You mean Daisy Kornfeld. Kind of homely. Just down the block. 712. Miss Duluth, I certainly ..."

"Thanks," cut in Iris and we were off again with our ever growing escort.

Daisy was sitting in the Kornfeld parlour, glumly thumping the piano. Ushered in by an excited, cooing Mrs. Kornfeld, Iris interrupted Daisy's rendition of *The Jolly Farmer*.

"Daisy, that picture you took of me yesterday to sell to Mr. Stone, is it developed yet?"

"Gee, no, Mith Duluth. I ain't got the developing money yet. Theventy-five thenth. Ma don't give me but a nickel an hour for practithing thith piano."

"Here." Iris thrust a ten-dollar bill into her hand. "I'll buy the whole roll. Run get the camera. We'll have it developed right away."

"Gee." The mercenary Daisy stared with blank incredulity at the ten-dollar bill.

I stared just as blankly myself. I wasn't being bright at all.

I wasn't much brighter an hour later. We were back in our apartment, waiting for Inspector Green. Poppy, all for love, was trying to climb into my lap. Iris, who had charmed Barney Stone into developing Daisy's film, clutched the yellow envelope of snaps in her hand. She had sent our policeman away on a secret mission, but an infuriating passion for the dramatic had kept her from telling or showing me anything. I had to wait for Inspector Green.

Eventually Iris' policeman returned and whispered with her in the hall. Then Inspector Green came. He looked cold and hostile. Poppy didn't like him. She growled. Sometimes Poppy was smart.

Inspector Green said, "You've been running all over town. I told you to stay here."

"I know." Iris' voice was meek. "It's just that I wanted to solve poor Miss Crump's poisoning."

"Solve it?" Inspector Green's query was skeptical.

"Yes. It's awfully simple really. I can't

imagine why we didn't think of it from the start."

"You mean you know who poisoned her?"

"Of course." Iris smiled, a maddening smile. "Henry Blodgett."

"But ..."

"Check with the airlines. I think you'll find that Blodgett flew in from Ogden Bluffs a few days ago and flew back today. As for his being sick in bed under his wife's care, I guess that'll make Mrs. Blodgett an accessory before the fact, won't it?"

Inspector Green was pop-eyed.

"Oh, it's my fault really," continued Iris. "I said no one came to the house yesterday except those three people. There was someone else, but he was so ordinary, so run-of-the-mill, that I forgot him completely."

I was beginning to see then. Inspector Green snapped, "And this run-of-the-mill character?"

"The man," said Iris sweetly, "who had the best chance of all to poison the hamburger, *the man who delivered it* —the man from the Supermarket.

"We don't have to guess. We have proof." Iris fumbled in the yellow envelope. "Yesterday morning as we were going out, we bumped into the man delivering Miss Crump's groceries. Just at that moment, a sweet little girl took a snap of us. This snap."

She selected a print and handed it to Inspector Green. I moved to look at it over his shoulder.

"I'm afraid Daisy is an impressionistic photographer," murmured Iris. "That hip on the right is me. The buttocks are my husband. But the figure in the middle—quite a masterly likeness of Henry Blodgett, isn't it? Of course, there's the grocery apron, the unshaven chin ..."

She was right. Daisy had only winged Iris and me but with the grocery man she had scored a direct hit. And the grocery man was unquestionably Henry Blodgett.

Iris nodded to her policeman. "Sergeant Blair took a copy of the snap around the neighbourhood groceries. They recognized Blodgett at the Supermarket. They hired him day before yesterday. He made a few deliveries this morning, including Miss Crump's, and took a powder without his pay."

"Well ..." stammered Inspector Green. "Well ..."

"Just how many charges can you get him on?" asked my wife hopefully. "Attempted homicide, conspiracy to defraud, illegal possession of poisonous drugs ... I hope you give him the works when you get him."

"We'll get him, all right," said Inspector Green.

Iris leaned over and patted Poppy's head affectionately.

"Don't worry, darling. I'm sure Miss Crump will get well and we'll throw a lovely christening party for your little strangers ..."

Iris was right about the Blodgetts. Henry got the works. And his wife was held as an accessory. Iris was right about Miss Crump too. She is still in the hospital but improving steadily and will almost certainly be well enough to attend the christening party.

Meanwhile, at her request, Poppy is staying with us, awaiting maternity with rollicking unconcern.

It's nice having a dog who pays the rent.

▲▼▶▼▶▲▼▶▼▶▲▼▶▼▶▲▼▶▼▶▲▼▶▼▶

STRANGE JEST

by Agatha Christie

Sweet, elderly, and gentle are hardly the qualities you'd look for in a detective. Yet Miss Marple from St. Mary Mead is all of those things, and she has no equal when it comes to solving mysteries!

And this," said Jane Helier, completing her introductions, "is Miss Marple!"

Being an actress, she was able to make her point. It was clearly the climax, the triumphant finale! Her tone was equally compounded of reverent awe and triumph.

The odd part of it was that the object thus proudly proclaimed was merely a gentle elderly spinster. In the eyes of the two young people who had just, by Jane's good offices, made her acquaintance, there showed incredulity and a tinge of dismay. They were nice-looking people—the girl, Charmian Stroud, slim and dark; the man, Edward Rossiter, a fair-haired, amiable young giant.

Charmian said, a little breathlessly, "Oh, we're awfully pleased to meet you." But there was doubt in her eyes. She flung a quick, questioning glance at Jane Helier.

"Darling," said Jane, answering the glance, "she's absolutely marvellous. Leave it to her. I told you I'd get her here and I have." She added to Miss Marple: "You'll fix it for them, I know. It will be easy for you."

Miss Marple turned her placid, china-blue eyes toward Mr. Rossiter. "Won't you tell me," she said, "what all this is about?"

"Jane's a friend of ours," Charmian broke in impatiently. "Edward and I are in rather a fix. Jane said if we would come to her party, she'd introduce us to someone who was—who would—who could—"

Edward came to the rescue. "Jane tells us you're the last word in sleuths, Miss Marple!"

The old lady's eyes twinkled, but she protested modestly: "Oh no, no! Nothing of the kind. It's just that living in a village as I do, one gets to know so much about human nature. But really you have made me quite curious. Do tell me your problem."

"I'm afraid it's terribly hackneyed—just buried treasure," said Edward.

"Indeed? But that sounds most exciting!"

"I know. Like Treasure Island. But our problem lacks the usual romantic touches. No point on a chart indicated by a skull and crossbones, no directions like 'four paces to the left, west by north.' It's horribly prosaic—just where we ought to dig."

"Have you tried at all?"

"I should say we'd dug about two solid acres! The whole place is ready to be turned into a market garden. We're just discussing whether to grow vegetable marrows or potatoes."

Charmian said, rather abruptly, "May we really tell you all about it?"

"But, of course, my dear."

"Then let's find a peaceful spot. Come on, Edward." She led the way out of the overcrowded and smoke-laden room, and they went up the stairs, to a small sitting-room on the second floor.

When they were seated, Charmian began abruptly: "Well, here goes! The story starts with Uncle Mathew, uncle—or rather, great-great-uncle—to both of us. He was incredibly ancient. Edward and I were his only relations. He was fond of us and always declared that when he died he would leave his money between us. Well, he died last March and left everything he had to be divided equally between Edward and myself. What I've just said sounds rather callous—I don't mean that it was right that he died—actually we were very fond of him. But he'd been ill for some time.

"The point is that the 'everything' he left turned out to be practically nothing at all. And that, frankly, was a bit of a blow to us both, wasn't it, Edward?"

The amiable Edward agreed. "You see," he said, "we'd counted on it a bit. I mean, when you know a good bit of money is coming to you, you don't—well—buckle down and try to make it yourself. I'm in the Army—not got anything to speak of outside my pay—and Charmian herself hasn't got a bean. She works as a stage manager in a repertory theatre—quite interesting and she enjoys it—but no money in it. We'd counted on getting married but weren't worried about the money side of it because we both knew we'd be jolly well off some day."

"And now, you see, we're not!" said Charmian. "What's more, Ansteys—that's the family place, and Edward and I both love it—will probably have to be sold. And Edward and I feel we just can't bear that! But if we don't find Uncle Mathew's money, we shall have to sell."

Edward said, "You know, Charmian, we still haven't come to the vital point."

"Well, you talk then."

Edward turned to Miss Marple. "It's like this, you see. As Uncle Mathew grew older, he got more and more suspicious. He didn't trust anybody."

"Very wise of him," said Miss Marple. "The depravity of human nature is unbelievable."

"Well, you may be right. Anyway, Uncle Mathew thought so. He had a friend who lost his money in a bank and another friend who was ruined by an absconding solicitor, and he lost some money himself in a fraudulent company. He got so

that he used to hold forth at great length that the
only safe and sane thing to do was to convert your
money into solid bullion and bury it."

"Ah," said Miss Marple. "I begin to see."

"Yes. Friends argued with him, pointed out
that he'd get no interest that way, but he held that
that didn't really matter. The bulk of your money,
he said, should be 'kept in a box under the bed or
buried in the garden.' Those were his words."

Charmian went on: "And when he died, he
left hardly anything at all in securities, though he
was very rich. So we think that that's what he must
have done."

Edward explained: "We found that he had
sold securities and drawn out large sums of money
from time to time, and nobody knows what he did
with them. But it seems probable that he lived up
to his principles and that he did buy gold and bury
it."

"He didn't say anything before he died?
Leave any paper? No letter?"

"That's the maddening part of it. He didn't.
He'd been unconscious for some days, but he
rallied before he died. He looked at us both and
chuckled—a faint, weak little chuckle. He said,
'You'll be all right, my pretty pair of doves.' And
then he tapped his eye—his right eye—and winked
at us. And then—he died.... Poor old Uncle
Mathew."

"He tapped his eye," said Miss Marple
thoughtfully.

Edward said eagerly, "Does that convey anything to you? It made me think of an Arsène Lupin story where there was something hidden in a man's glass eye. But Uncle Mathew didn't have a glass eye."

Miss Marple shook her head. "No—I can't think of anything at the moment."

Charmian said, disappointedly, "Jane told us you'd say at once where to dig!"

Miss Marple smiled. "I'm not quite a conjurer, you know. I didn't know your uncle, or what sort of man he was, and I don't know the house or the grounds."

Charmian said, "If you did know them?"

"Well, it must be quite simple really, mustn't it?" said Miss Marple.

"Simple!" said Charmian. "You come down to Ansteys and see if it's simple!"

It is possible that she did not mean the invitation to be taken seriously, but Miss Marple said briskly, "Well, really, my dear, that's very kind of you. I've always wanted to have the chance of looking for buried treasure. And," she added, looking at them with a beaming, late-Victorian smile, "with a love interest too!"

"You see!" said Charmian, gesturing dramatically.

They had just completed a grand tour of Ansteys. They had been round the kitchen garden—heavily trenched. They had been through the little woods, where every important tree had been dug round, and had gazed sadly on the pitted surface of the once smooth lawn. They had been up to the attic, where old trunks and chests had been rifled of their contents. They had been down to the cellars, where flagstones had been heaved unwillingly from their sockets. They had measured and tapped walls, and Miss Marple had been shown every antique piece of furniture that contained or could be suspected of containing a secret drawer.

On a table in the morning room there was a heap of papers—all the papers that the late Mathew Stroud had left. Not one had been destroyed, and Charmian and Edward were wont to return to them again and again, earnestly perusing bills, invitations, and business correspondence in the hope of spotting a hitherto unnoticed clue.

"Can you think of anywhere we haven't looked?" demanded Charmian hopefully.

Miss Marple shook her head. "You seem to have been very thorough, my dear. Perhaps, if I may say so, just a little too thorough. I always think, you know, that one should have a plan. It's like my friend, Mrs. Eldritch; she had such a nice little maid, polished linoleum beautifully, but she was so thorough that she polished the bathroom floors too much, and as Mrs. Eldritch was stepping out of the bath the cork mat slipped from under her and she had a very nasty fall and actually broke her leg! Most awkward, because the bathroom door was locked, of course, and the gardener had to get a ladder and come in through the window—terribly distressing to Mrs. Eldritch, who had always been a very modest woman."

Edward moved restlessly.

Miss Marple said quickly, "Please forgive me. So apt, I know, to fly off at a tangent. But one thing does remind one of another. And sometimes that is helpful. All I was trying to say was that perhaps if we tried to sharpen our wits and think of a likely place—"

Edward said crossly, "You think of one, Miss Marple. Charmian's brains and mine are now only beautiful blanks!"

"Dear, dear. Of course—most tiring for you. If you don't mind I'll just look through all this." She indicated the papers on the table. "That is, if there's nothing private—I don't want to appear to pry."

"Oh, that's all right. But I'm afraid you won't find anything."

She sat down by the table and methodically worked through the sheaf of documents. As she replaced each one, she sorted them automatically into tidy little heaps. When she had finished she sat staring in front of her for some minutes.

Edward asked, not without a touch of malice, "Well, Miss Marple?"

She came to herself with a little start. "I beg your pardon. Most helpful."

"You've found something relevant?"

"Oh no, nothing like that, but I do believe I know what sort of man your Uncle Mathew was.

Rather like my own Uncle Henry, I think. Fond of rather obvious jokes. A bachelor, evidently—I wonder why—perhaps an early disappointment? Methodical up to a point, but not very fond of being tied up—so few bachelors are!"

Behind Miss Marple's back Charmian made a sign to Edward. It said, "She's ga-ga."

Miss Marple was continuing happily to talk of her deceased Uncle Henry. "Very fond of puns, he was. And to some people puns are most annoying. A mere play upon words may be very irritating. He was a suspicious man too. Always was convinced the servants were robbing him. And sometimes, of course, they were, but not always. It grew upon him, poor man. Toward the end he suspected them of tampering with his food and finally refused to eat anything but boiled eggs! Dear Uncle Henry, he used to be such a merry soul at one time—very fond of his coffee after dinner. He always used to say, 'This coffee is very Moorish,' meaning, you know, that he'd like a little more."

Edward felt that if he heard any more about Uncle Henry he'd go mad.

"Fond of young people, too," went on Miss Marple, "but inclined to tease them a little, if you know what I mean. Used to put bags of sweets where a child just couldn't reach them."

Casting politeness aside, Charmian said, "I think he sounds horrible!"

"Oh no, dear, just an old bachelor, you know, and not used to children. And he wasn't at all stupid, really. He used to keep a good deal of money in the house, and he had a safe put in. Made a great fuss about it—and how very secure it was. As a result of his talking so much, burglars broke in one night and actually cut a hole in the safe with a chemical device."

"Served him right," said Edward.

"Oh, but there was nothing in the safe," said Miss Marple. "You see, he really kept the money somewhere else—behind some volumes of sermons in the library, as a matter of fact. He said people never took a book of that kind out of the shelf."

Edward interrupted excitedly, "I say, that's an idea. What about the library?"

But Charmian shook a scornful head. "Do you think I hadn't thought of that? I went through all the books Tuesday of last week, when you went off to Portsmouth. Took them all out, shook them. Nothing there."

Edward sighed. Then, rousing himself, he endeavoured to rid himself tactfully of their disappointing guest. "It's been awfully good of you to come down as you have and try to help us. Sorry it's been all a washout. Feel we trespassed a lot on your time. However, I'll get the car out and you'll be able to catch the three-thirty—"

"Oh," said Miss Marple, "but we've got to find the money, haven't we? You mustn't give up, Mr. Rossiter. 'If at first you don't succeed, try, try, try again.'"

"You mean you're going to go—on trying?"

"Strictly speaking," said Miss Marple, "I haven't begun yet. 'First catch your hare,' as Mrs. Beeton says in her cookery book—a wonderful book but terribly expensive; most of the recipes begin, 'Take a quart of cream and a dozen eggs.' Let me see, where was I? Oh yes. Well, we have, so to speak, caught our hare—the hare being, of course, your Uncle Mathew, and we've only got to decide now where he would have hidden the money. It ought to be quite simple."

"Simple?" demanded Charmian.

"Oh yes, dear. I'm sure he would have done the obvious thing. A secret drawer—that's my solution."

Edward said dryly, "You couldn't put bars of gold in a secret drawer."

"No, no, of course not. But there's no reason to believe the money is in gold."

"He always used to say—"

"So did my Uncle Henry about his safe! So I should strongly suspect that that was just a simple blind. Diamonds, now they could be in a secret drawer quite easily."

"But we've looked in all the secret drawers. We had a cabinetmaker over to examine the furniture."

"Did you, dear? That was clever of you. I should suggest your uncle's own desk would be the most likely. Was it the tall escritoire against the wall there?"

"Yes. And I'll show you." Charmian went

over to it. She took down the flap. Inside were pigeonholes and little drawers. She opened a small door in the centre and touched a spring inside the left-hand drawer. The bottom of the centre recess clicked and slid forward. Charmian drew it out, revealing a shallow well beneath. It was empty.

"Now isn't that a coincidence," exclaimed Miss Marple. "Uncle Henry had a desk just like this one, only his was burr walnut and this is mahogany."

"At any rate," said Charmian, "there's nothing there, as you can see."

"I expect," said Miss Marple, "your cabinetmaker was a young man. He didn't know everything. People were very artful when they made hiding places in those days. There's such a thing as a secret inside a secret."

She extracted a hairpin from her neat bun of grey hair. Straightening it out, she stuck the point into what appeared to be a tiny wormhole in one side of the secret recess. With a little difficulty she pulled out a small drawer. In it was a bundle of faded letters and a folded paper.

Edward and Charmian pounced on the find together. With trembling fingers Edward unfolded the paper. He dropped it with an exclamation of disgust.

"A cookery recipe. Baked ham!"

Charmian was untying a ribbon that held the letters together. She drew one out and glanced at it. "Love letters!"

Miss Marple reacted with Victorian gusto. "How interesting! Perhaps the reason your uncle never married."

Charmian read aloud:

"My ever dear Mathew, I must confess that the time seems long indeed since I received your last letter. I try to occupy myself with the various tasks allotted to me, and often say to myself that I am indeed fortunate to see so much of the globe, though little did I think when I went to America that I should voyage off to these far islands!"

Charmian broke off. "Where is it from? Oh, Hawaii!" She went on:

"Alas, these natives are still far from seeing the light. They are in an unclothed and savage state and spend most of their time swimming and dancing, adorning themselves with garlands of flowers. Mr. Gray has made some converts but it is uphill work, and he and Mrs. Gray get sadly discouraged. I try to do all I can to cheer and encourage him, but I, too, am often sad for a reason you can guess, dear Mathew. Alas, absence is a severe trial for a loving heart. Your renewed vows and protestations of affection cheered me greatly. Now and always you have my faithful and devoted heart, dear Mathew, and I remain—

Your true love,
Betty Martin

"P.S.—I address my letter under cover to our mutual friend, Matilda Graves, as usual. I hope Heaven will pardon this little subterfuge."

Edward whistled. "A female missionary! So that was Uncle Mathew's romance. I wonder why they never married?"

"She seems to have gone all over the world," said Charmian, looking through the letters. "Mauritius—all sorts of places. Probably died of yellow fever or something."

A gentle chuckle made them start. Miss Marple was apparently much amused. "Well, well," she said. "Fancy that, now!"

She was reading the recipe for baked ham. Seeing their inquiring glances, she read out: " 'Baked Ham with Spinach. Take a nice piece of gammon, stuff with cloves and cover with brown sugar. Bake in a slow oven. Serve with a border of puréed spinach.'

"What do you think of that now?"

"I think it sounds filthy," said Edward.

"No, no, actually it would be very good—but what do you think of the whole thing?"

A sudden ray of light illuminated Edward's face. "Do you think it's a code—cryptogram of some kind?" He seized it.

"Look here, Charmian, it might be, you know! No reason to put a cooking recipe in a secret drawer otherwise."

"Exactly," said Miss Marple. "Very, very significant."

Charmian said, "I know what it might be—invisible ink! Let's heat it. Turn on the electric fire."

Edward did so. But no signs of writing appeared under the treatment.

Miss Marple coughed. "I really think, you know, that you're making it rather too difficult. The recipe is only an indication, so to speak. It is, I think, the letters that are significant."

"The letters?"

"Especially," said Miss Marple, "the signature."

But Edward hardly heard her. He called excitedly, "Charmian! Come here! She's right. See—the envelopes are old right enough, but the letters themselves were written much later."

"Exactly," said Miss Marple.

"They're only fake old. I bet anything old Uncle Mat faked them himself—"

"Precisely," said Miss Marple.

"The whole thing's a sell. There never was a female missionary. It must be a code."

"My dear, dear children—there's really no need to make it all so difficult. Your uncle was really a very simple man. He had to have his little joke, that was all."

For the first time they gave her their full attention. "Just exactly what do you mean, Miss Marple?" asked Charmian.

"I mean, dear, that you're actually holding the

money in your hand this minute."

Charmian stared down.

"The signature, dear. That gives the whole thing away. The recipe is just an indication. Shorn of all the cloves and brown sugar and the rest of it, what is it actually? Why, gammon and spinach to be sure! Gammon and spinach! Meaning— nonsense! So it's clear that it's the letters that are important. And then, if you take into consideration what your uncle did just before he died. He tapped his eye, you said. Well, there you are—that gives you the clue, you see."

Charmian said, "Are we mad, or are you?"

"Surely, my dear, you must have heard the expression meaning that something is not a true picture, or has it quite died out nowadays: *'All my eye and Betty Martin.'* "

Edward gasped, his eyes falling to the letter in his hand. "Betty Martin—"

"Of course, Mr. Rossiter. As you have just said, there isn't—there wasn't any such person. The letters were written by your uncle, and I dare say he got a lot of fun out of writing them! As you say, the writing on the envelopes is much older—in fact, the envelopes couldn't belong to the letters anyway, because the postmark of the one you are holding is eighteen fifty-one."

She paused. She made it very emphatic: "Eighteen fifty-one. And that explains everything, doesn't it?"

"Not to me," said Edward.

"Well, of course," said Miss Marple. "I dare say it wouldn't to me if it weren't for my great-nephew Lionel. Such a dear little boy and a passionate stamp collector. Knows all about stamps. It was he who told me about rare and expensive stamps and that a wonderful new find had come up for auction. And I actually remember his mentioning one stamp—an 1851 blue 2 cent. It realized something like $25 000, I believe. Fancy! I should imagine that the other stamps are something also rare and expensive. No doubt your uncle bought through dealers and was careful to 'cover his tracks,' as they say in detective stories."

Edward groaned. He sat down and buried his face in his hands.

"What's the matter?" demanded Charmian.

"Nothing. It's only the awful thought that, but for Miss Marple, we might have burned these letters in a decent, gentlemanly way!"

"Ah," said Miss Marple, "that's just what these old gentlemen who are fond of their joke never realize. My Uncle Henry, I remember, sent a favourite niece a five-pound note for a Christmas present. He put it inside a Christmas card, gummed the card together, and wrote on it: 'Love and best wishes. Afraid this is all I can manage this year.'

"She, poor girl, was annoyed at what she thought was his meanness and threw it all straight into the fire. So then, of course, he had to give her another."

Edward's feelings toward Uncle Henry had suffered an abrupt and complete change.

"Miss Marple," he said, "I'm going to get a bottle of champagne. We'll all drink the health of your Uncle Henry."

ACKNOWLEDGEMENTS

Permission to reprint copyright material is gratefully acknowledged. Every reasonable effort to trace the copyright holders of materials appearing in this book has been made. Information that will enable the publisher to rectify any error or omission will be welcomed.

The Chocolate Mousse Murder by Marty Norman. Appeared in *Murder Ink*, copyright ©1984, 1977 by Workman Publishing Company, Inc. Reprinted by permission of the artist.

Bog Body by Katherine Grier from *Discover: Mysteries of the Past and Present — A Royal Ontario Museum Book*. Text copyright © 1989 by The Royal Ontario Museum. Reprinted by permission of Kids Can Press Ltd., Toronto, Canada. Available in the United States from Addison-Wesley. Reprinted by permission of Addison-Wesley Publishing Co., Inc. Reading, MA.

Live Music © Adèle Geras 1984 from *Letters of Fire and Other Unsettling Stories*, Hamish Hamilton, London. Reprinted by permission of the author.

The Boy From Nowhere from the book *The Screaming Scull* by William E. Warren © 1987. Used by permission of the publisher, Simon & Schuster Books for Young Readers, New York.

The Summer of the Beautiful White Horse from *My Name Is Aram*, copyright 1938 and renewed 1966 by William Saroyan, reprinted by permission of Harcourt Brace & Company.

Midnight by Baljit Kang, an award-winning entry in the 1983 W H Smith Young Writers' Competition from *Young Writers*, 25th Year (Heinemann Educational Books).

Two Stories to Solve: Text of "Outwitting the King" and "The Bet" from *More Stories to Solve* by George Shannon. Text copyright © 1989, 1990 by George W. B. Shannon. By permission of Greenwillow Books, a division of William Morrow & Co., Inc.

Lamb to the Slaughter from *Someone Like You* by Roald Dahl. Copyright 1953 by Roald Dahl. Reprinted by permission of Alfred A. Knopf, Inc.

Twins © copyright Eric Wright 1990. First published in *A Suit of Diamonds* (HarperCollins Publishers U.K. Ltd.).

ACKNOWLEDGEMENTS

Appears here by arrangement with Bella Pomer Agency Inc.

Origin of the Detective Business by Newton Newkirk from *Murderess Ink*. Copyright © 1979 by Workman Publishing Company, Inc.

The Big Holdup from *Aha!*, by Martin Gardner. Copyright © 1978 by Scientific American, Inc. Reprinted by permission of W.H. Freeman and Company.

The Punchboards by Henry T. Parry; Copyright © 1983 by Henry T. Parry; reprinted by permission of the author.

Fingerprints Tell Tales by Martha G. Webb from *Murderess Ink*. Copyright © 1979 by Workman Publishing Company, Inc.

The Case of the Dentist's Patient from *Two-Minute Mysteries* copyright © 1967 by Donald J. Sobol. Used by permission of Scholastic, Inc.

Puzzle for Poppy reprinted by permission of Curtis Brown, Ltd. Copyright © 1946 by Patrick Quentin. Originally printed in Ellery Queen's Mystery Magazine. Copyright renewed 1974.

Strange Jest by Agatha Christie. From *Three Blind Mice and Other Stories* (U.S.) and *Miss Marple's Final Cases* (Canada) by permission of the Putnam Publishing Group and Harold Ober Associates Incorporated. Copyright © 1941 by Agatha Christie. Copyright renewed 1969 by Agatha Christie Mallowan.

THE EDITORS

James Barry is Chairman of the English Department at Brebeuf College School, North York, Ontario. He is the editor of the poetry anthologies *Themes on the Journey, Departures,* and *Side by Side: Songs and Poems,* as well as an annual student writing anthology, *Triple Bronze.* Besides teaching, his special interests are sports (especially hockey), music, and student writing.

Christine McClymont was born in Scotland, but came to Canada at an early age. For many years, she has been compiling anthologies for Nelson series such as *Networks, In Context,* and *Features.* When she is not reading or writing, Christine enjoys hiking and cross-country skiing, and is actively involved with the Toronto Chamber Society.

Glen Huser, a former teacher and librarian, is a learning resources consultant for the Edmonton Public School Board. He has won several newspaper literary competitions, and his novel, *Grace Lake,* was nominated for the W. H. Smith/Books in Canada First Novel Award in 1990. He also edits *Magpie,* magazine of student writing and graphics.